THE P[...]
CHILD[...] ANTHOLOGY

The earth is ours

Poems for secondary schools

**Selected and introduced by
Ian Gordon**

POETRY LIBRARY
SOUTH BANK CENTRE
ROYAL FESTIVAL HALL
LONDON
SE1 8XX

MACMILLAN

© Copyright text Ian Gordon 1994
© Copyright illustrations The Macmillan Press Ltd 1994

All rights reserved. No reproduction, copy or transmission of
this publication may be made without written permission.

No paragraph of this publication may be reproduced, copied or
transmitted save with written permission or in accordance with
the provisions of the Copyright, Designs and Patents Act 1988,
or under the terms of any licence permitting limited copying issued
by the Copyright Licensing Agency, 90 Tottenham Court Road,
London W1P 9HE.

Any person who does any unauthorised act in relation to this
publication may be liable to criminal prosecution and civil
claims for damages.

First published 1994

Published by THE MACMILLAN PRESS LTD
London and Basingstoke
*Associated companies and representatives in Accra,
Auckland, Delhi, Dublin, Gaborone, Hamburg, Harare,
Hong Kong, Kuala Lumpur, Lagos, Manzini, Melbourne,
Mexico City, Nairobi, New York, Singapore, Tokyo.*

ISBN 0-333-54214-2

Printed in Hong Kong

A catalogue record for this book is available from the
British Library.

Contents

Introduction   1

Against poems: For poems Nadir Tharani   10

The story inside   12

Bezuidenhout Damian Ruth   13
The Lagos-Ibadan road before Shagamu John Pepper Clark   15
Food for the couple Mafika Gwala   16
One for the road Charles Mungoshi   16
What has happened to Lulu? Charles Causley   17
Ballad of the landlord Langston Hughes   19
The other time Peter Appleton   20
Jonah and the whale Gareth Owen   21
Ballad of the bread man Charles Causley   24

Faces of love   28

My baby has no name yet Kim Nam Jo   29
Beloved of my mother Okot p'Bitek   29
Isatou died Lenrie Peters   30
Grandma at 90 o'clock Eddison Zvogbo   31
Mama and daughter Langston Hughes   33
Love is Mervyn Morris   34
Two songs Berber, Morocco   34
Serenade Philippa Namutebi Barlow   35
The mesh Kwesi Brew   36
The eyes that wouldn't wander Laban Erapu   36
The crack Sheikha El-Miskery   37
Confession Christopher van Wyk   37
Like a flame Grace Nichols   38
Mourning song (three translations)   39
   H.A. Giles, Arthur Waley, Ezra Pound
Wedding eve Everett Standa   40
A senryu sequence Traditional, Japan   41
New face Alice Walker   42
Letter from a contract worker Antonio Jacinto   43

Working days 46

Work D.H. Lawrence 46
The palm-wine tapper's song Segun Sofowote 47
Reapers in a mieliefield Mbuyiseni Oswald Mtshali 48
Paddy rice song Konishi Raizan 49
Song of agony Gouveia de Lemos 49
From Islands Edward Kamau Brathwaite 50
Song of the wagondriver B.S. Johnson 52
Woman work Maya Angelou 53
Career woman Charles Mungoshi 54
Daydream Jeanette Leboent Kassam 55
The woman I married Edwin Waiyaki 55
Hunting for a job Elias Nyakunu 56

The price of freedom 58

Colonizer's logic Chinweizu 59
Stanley meets Mutesa David Rubadiri 59
The weaver bird Kofi Awoonor 61
The making of a servant J.J.R. Jolobe 61
There was an Indian John Squire 63
Still I rise Maya Angelou 64
To Mai Musaemura Bonas Zimunya 66
Touch Hugh Lewin 67
From Letters to Martha Dennis Brutus 69
Another day Hugh Lewin 70
In detention Christopher van Wyk 72
The laying of the stones Daniel P. Kunene 73
The newest bride Henry Barlow 74
A freedom song Marjorie Oludhe Macgoye 76

Modern living 80

What's wrong with people? Mongane Serote 81
Once upon a time Gabriel Imomotime Okara 81
African dancing Eric Mazani 83
The street Jared Angira 84
An abandoned bundle Mbuyiseni Oswald Mtshali 85
Neon Amin Kassam 86
Lost friends Lenrie Peters 86
Justice is done Oumar Ba 88
Corruption Freddy Macha 89
A prescription for development Cecil Rajendra 90

From *Song of Ocol* Okot p'Bitek   92
A *pregnant schoolgirl* Everett Standa   94

The natural world   96

Kob antelope Yoruba, Nigeria   97
A leopard lives in a muu tree Jonathan Kariara   99
Bats Randall Jarrell   99
Guardian fly Anthony Nazombe   100
Animals Walt Whitman   101
Carrion crows A.J. Seymour   101
Hawk roosting Ted Hughes   102
The song of the whale Kit Wright   103
The red cockatoo Anonymous, China   104
An African thunderstorm David Rubadiri   104
August break Okogbule Wonodi   106
The dry season Kwesi Brew   106
Hymn to the sea Frank Collymore   107

This is war   110

Battle hymn Acholi, Uganda   111
The white horse Tu Fu   112
Geography lesson Zulfikar Ghose   113
Refugee mother and child Chinua Achebe   114
Moon in the bucket Gabriel Imomotime Okara   115
Voices Ken Saro-Wiwa   115
Conquerors Henry Treece   116
A war-torn wife Chenjerai Hove   116
Tramp Frank Chipasula   118
Today Chiwa P. Chipeya   119
If I die in war Spike Milligan   119

Reflections   122

The pond Mervyn Morris   123
Forefathers Birago Diop   124
Dreams Langston Hughes   125
Burning log Charles Mungoshi   125
Changing the wheel Bertold Brecht   125
New Year's Day Cecil Rajendra   126
The new platform dances Jack Mapanje   127
Lies Yevgeny Yevtushenko   128
Five ways to kill a man Edwin Brock   129

The people's creed Canaan Banana   130
Thank you, Lord Maya Angelou   131

Acknowledgements   134

Detailed advice on teaching the poems in this anthology, plus suggestions for further activities can be found in **The Earth is Ours: Teacher's Notes** which accompanies this anthology. A copy is available free of charge with every class set.

Introduction

A poem can be about anything. The rich variety of poems in this collection shows this well. The first 'story' poem, set in a South African courtroom, tells a tragic tale of murder of one brother by another, and the suffering caused by the courtroom judgement. The last poem, by Maya Angelou, is a prayer of thanks and hope in the face of harsh experience. Between, there are poems which are tender evocations of love, celebrations of nature, condemnations of the evils of society, calls for freedom, and much else.

What makes a poem is not what it is about, but how the writer approaches the subject. A poem may make us think more deeply, and a poem always appeals strongly to our feelings. But to do this in just a few words, a writer must be able to use all the resources of language. Many of the techniques a poet uses are employed in other kinds of writing – stories, letters, articles, essays, for example. But in poetry the techniques are vitally important, for poetry is an intense form of expression, and a poet must create effects quickly and powerfully.

There are two reasons why it is well worthwhile studying some of the most common literary techniques. In the first place this will help you to get more out of your reading of poetry, just as you appreciate a sports match more if you know something about the rules of the game. But perhaps more importantly this knowledge will help you in your own writing. Not everyone can be a great writer, but everyone can write something, for everyone thinks, feels and has language.

Whether a poem is from the oral tradition (poems by unknown authors handed down in spoken form from generation to generation) or the literary tradition (poems written by known authors and meant to be read in print), it should always be read aloud. The sound of a poem is always important. A poem needs to be performed.

How a poem sounds

RHYME is the most powerful way of echoing sound and binding lines of poetry together. It is the one writing technique used in poetry, but not in other types of writing. Words rhyme fully if their final stressed syllables sound the same: *hat / mat; free / be*. Full rhyme sounds richer when the words end in two consonants: *grasp / clasp*, or if the vowels are diphthongs (two 'pure' vowel sounds run together): *oil / boil*. Even richer rhymes are achieved with diphthongs and double final consonants: *taste / waste*. With longer words, the rhyme may be in more than one syllable: *parted / started*. Poets using full rhyme vary this richness to suit their purposes.

A pair of lines which rhyme fully is called a COUPLET. Here are two couplets from *Woman work*, page 53:

> I've got the children to tend
> The clothes to mend
> The floor to mop
> The food to shop

Full rhyme has been used in English poetry for hundreds of years and many poets still use it. *Isatou died* (page 30), for example, provides an excellent example of the skilful use of full rhyme by a modern African poet. But in modern times, IMPERFECT RHYME (sometimes called HALF RHYME) has been more widely used than full rhyme. *Heat / delicate* and *orderly / gallery* are typical examples of imperfect rhymes. And in much modern poetry rhyme is not used at all.

ALLITERATION, the close repetition of the same consonant sound, is another powerful device for binding words together. See how effective the repeated *r* and *b* sounds are in this line:

> And the *r*ed *r*oofs *b*urn more *b*rightly against her *b*lue
>   *Hymn to the sea*, (page 107)

In these two lines it is *w* that is repeated:

> The year is *w*ithering; the *w*ind
> Blo*w*s down the leaves.
>   *The dry season* (page 106)

And here is another good example of alliteration from *Stanley meets Mutesa* (page 59, line 16):

> Flies *cl*ung in *cl*umps on their *s*weat-*s*cented backs.

The repeated heavy *cl* sound suggests the feeling of men carrying wearying loads in the scorching African sun. The repetition of the *s* sound (called SIBILANCE) is likewise effective. This repetition draws our attention to *sweat-scented*. Notice also how impossible it is to speak this line quickly. The many consonants slow us down – as the men were slowed down under their loads.

ASSONANCE is the close repetition of the same vowel sound. The bold first line of *The crack* (page 37) provides an excellent example: 'Cr*a*ck the gl*a*ss'. Assonance is generally not so noticeable as alliteration, but skilful use of assonance can contribute to the music of a poem.

Our everyday speech has a natural RHYTHM; we stress some words and syllables more than others. A poet organises the words of a poem to make the rhythm reinforce the meaning.

Sometimes this rhythm is quite regular. Regular rhythm in poetry is called METRE, and the most common metre in English poetry is an unstressed syllable followed by a stressed one. This is called an IAMBIC rhythm:

> Two *nights* a *week* I *see* my *wife*,
> And *eat* a *decent meal*,
> But *otherwise*, for *all* my *life*,
> I'm *married to* my *wheel*.
> *Song of the wagon driver* (page 52)

This regular rhythm helps to suggest the monotony of the driver's work.

Most modern poems have a much less marked rhythm than this. But all skilful poets organise their lines so that the stress falls on the most important words and phrases and so that the rhythm and sense of the words are in harmony. They may arrange individual words in an unusual order for special effect; so *The palm-wine tapper's song* starts 'Like the bat I dance' rather than 'I dance like a bat'. This device is called INVERSION. This inversion makes 'bat' the first stressed word in the sentence and so emphasises it.

Choosing words and images

Poets, like all writers, are careful about word choice. They must choose just the right words for their purpose. For example, 'gaunt' and 'shambled' are just the right words in these lines from *Conquerors* (page 116):

> A gaunt dog started up from some dark place
> And shambled off on legs as thin as sticks

If a poet feels no word is just right, he may make one up. Such **COINAGES** are usually made by running two words together. 'lazylapping' in *Hymn to the sea* (page 107) is a good example, as is 'windruffed' ('ruffed' is a less common form of 'ruffled') two lines later. In *Corruption* (page 89) Freddy Macha makes up a completely new word: 'Somewhere along the table a fly zzzzz past ...' Words such as 'whisper' or 'murmur' or 'zzzzz' whose sound suggests their meaning are examples of **ONOMATOPOEIA**; they are onomatopaeic words.

When we read in *Song of Okol* (page 92):

> My spacious garden
> Explodes with jacaranda and rose

we understand that the flowers do not really explode in the way bombs explode. Okot p'Bitek is using **FIGURATIVE LANGUAGE**. 'Explodes' is being used figuratively, to give a vivid impression of sudden blossoming and colour.

Writers often bring their subjects to life by using vivid and maybe unusual comparisons. If the comparison states fully that one thing is 'like' another or 'as' another we call the comparison a **SIMILE**. So the traditional Acholi *Battle hymn* from Uganda (page 111) opens:

> We are poured on the enemy like a mighty torrent
> We are poured like a river in spate when the rain is in
>   the mountains.

These two similes are easy to understand, but some similes are quite startling, as when in *Wedding eve* (page 40) Everett Standa likens his bride to a 'clever passenger in a faulty plane'. You will have to read the whole poem to decide whether you think this is a good comparison or not!

When we use a **METAPHOR**, we do not say 'like' or 'as'. We boldly state one thing *is* another. So in *Dreams* (page 125),

Langston Hughes writes:

> . . . if dreams die
> Life is a broken-winged bird.

And Segun Sofowote in *The palm wine tapper's song* (page 47) uses metaphors when he says his palm tree is a 'one-pole hut'; an 'ugly giant', and an 'erect crocodile'.

A metaphor can continue for several lines, perhaps through the whole poem, as the poet develops an idea. This is called a **SUSTAINED METAPHOR**. *The Weaver Bird* (page 61), where the colonisers of Africa are compared to this intruding bird, is a good example of a sustained metaphor.

Sometimes a writer chooses to describe an emotion or an idea as if it were a person. For example, as we read *The newest bride* (page 74) by Henry Barlow we realise that his bride is not a woman but freedom. This device is called **PERSONIFICATION**. It can be used to make an idea or object seem more real and immediate.

Repeating key words and phrases

Repetition of words and phrases is one of the simplest literary devices, but it can also be very powerful. Repetition reinforces ideas in a poem and it can also give a poem shape. Just a glance at *Song of agony* (page 49) shows how 'Which of us . . .' and 'not seeing' are repeated. And reading the poem aloud reveals how effective this repetition is. In *Touch* (page 67), Hugh Lewin repeats 'touch', 'touched', 'untouched', 'untouchable' exploring the good and bad meanings these words can hold.

The repetition of one or two complete lines is called a **REFRAIN**: one good example is in *The song of the whale* (page 102):

> Lipstick for our painted faces
> Polish for our shoes

Another example is the refrain that concludes each stanza of *The making of a servant* (page 61):

> I have seen the making of a servant
> In the young yoke-ox.

Levels of meaning

When a poet wants to suggest further meanings behind the 'surface' meaning of his poem, he uses SYMBOLISM. For example, as we read *Hawk roosting* (page 102) we may come to feel that this poem is not just about a bird, but that the hawk symbolises some aspect of human nature or society; in *A leopard lives in a muu tree* (page 99) we may think that Jonathan Kariara is writing about something more than just a leopard. When Bertold Brecht writes about his feelings as a wheel is changed on a car in *Changing the wheel* (page 125) we feel that perhaps he is really concerned with his journey through life, not just one along a road.

When we speak or write ironically we mean just the opposite of what we seem to be saying. IRONY is a part of everyday speech. 'What a wonderful day!' may mean just the opposite – it may be an ironic comment on a day of disasters and disappointments. So when in *A prescription for development* (page 90), Cecil Rajendra describes pollution as 'the hallmark of development', we understand that pollution is not a mark of excellence (as is a hallmark stamped on gold or silver) but a mark of greed and inefficiency.

A poet may write directly in his or her own voice – or adopt the VOICE or 'mask' of another person. So the Nigerian writer Chinweizu in *Colonizer's Logic* (page 57) is obviously not the white coloniser who says:

> These natives are unintelligent –
> We can't understand their language.

In *Freedom Song* (page 76), Marjorie Oludhe Macgoye chooses to tell the story in the voice of the man of the family. A poet may even talk with the voice of an animal or bird as does Ted Hughes in his powerful *Hawk roosting* (page 102).

We need have no special knowledge to understand most poems. But sometimes a poet enriches his poem by ALLUSION – references to stories or facts that we need to know to understand the poem fully. So we have to know something about the Christian story in the New Testament to understand Chinua Achebe's reference to 'Madonna and Child' in the first line of his poem *Refugee mother and child* (page 114), or to the 'Baby in the Manger' in *An abandoned bundle* (page 85) or to understand the meaning of the *Ballad of the bread man*. In *Grandma at 90 o'clock* (page 31) we need to know the significance of Nagasaki, and of Egypt in the Old Testament.

A special form of allusion is **PARODY**. A parody imitates another poem or type of poem, for comic effect. *Guardian fly* (page 100) is a parody because it uses the style of a praise song to praise not a hero, but a humble fly.

Forms of poetry

A poem may be written in a special form which determines for example the number and length of lines, the rhythm, and the way the lines rhyme – some of those individual features which we looked at earlier.

The **SONNET** is one form of poem. A sonnet has fourteen lines. Each line has ten syllables arranged in a regular iambic rhythm. The lines follow a special rhyme scheme (the pattern the rhymes take through the poem). Sonnets were once very popular, and thousands of sonnets have been written in English. *There was an Indian* (page 63) is a good example of this form, and when you read it you may understand how effective sonnets can be.

The traditional **BALLAD** form is still sometimes used for narrative verse – poetry which tells a story. Each **STANZA** is of four lines (a stanza, or verse, is a group of lines in a poem). The first and third lines are generally of eight syllables. The second and fourth are generally of six syllables and these lines always rhyme. The rhythm is mainly iambic. However, in ballads the number of syllables may vary, and the rhythm is not always perfectly regular, as the opening stanza of *What has happened to Lulu?* (page 17) shows:

> What has happened to Lulu, mother?
> What has happened to Lu?
> There's nothing in her bed but an old rag-doll
> And by its side a shoe.

This poem and *Ballad of the breadman* are excellent examples of modern ballads.

A special traditional form comes from Japan, and is called the **SENRYU**. The senryu sequence on page 41 shows what these snapshots of life are like. A senryu consists of three lines and is about fifteen syllables long – but you need not worry too much about this or about the rhythm. It is the sharp observation that counts.

Most modern poems are written not in set forms but in **FREE VERSE**. In free verse, rhyme and half rhyme may be used but they are not essential. There is no need for a regular rhythm, but the rhythm should be in harmony with the sense, and the important words should be stressed. Lines can be of any length. The poem can be as long or short as the writer chooses, and may continue without break, or be divided into **VERSE PARAGRAPHS** of different lengths. Punctuation may be used sparingly, as in *Another day* (page 70), or even abandoned altogether, as in *In detention* (page 72). A writer of free verse may also experiment boldly with layout as we can see in *The street* (page 84).

This freedom is very exciting for a writer; but as a famous poet once said, 'no verse is really free for the writer who wants to write well'. Study closely poems written in free verse, and you will see that good ones are skilfully organised. Write some poems yourself. Try free verse to start with. Choose a subject you feel strongly about – perhaps some of the poems in this book will stimulate your ideas. Write honestly, but remember that writing is a craft. Use, as you need them, the techniques of writing you have just been reading about. Your thoughts and feelings can then be shared by your reader, just as you want them to be.

Words . . . Poems

Look after
the
and the
will
take care
of themselves

Roger McGough

The poems

Against poems

so I write about
armpits and sweat,
thighs and stones;
I indicate smells,
5 a mango,
convey the sound
that is with us every day;
I try to explain that
the earth is ours
10 and eyes can lie,
that the sun is yellow
and dust painful.
But tell me,
have you seen a word
15 break a rock?

For poems

words can't break stones
nor wash feet;
but then
how many stones or feet
20 can explain,
what our hands create
belongs to us.

Nadir Tharani *Tanzania*

The story inside

The story inside

From earliest times poets have responded to the strong human hunger for stories, including stories of death, passion and conflict. Nowadays we are more likely to find such stories in newspaper reports; it is interesting that the first two poems in this section refer directly to such reports. The third poem *Food for the couple* could easily be the sort of sad news item that we can read any day in the news columns.

■ We may perhaps imagine *One for the road* more as a newspaper photograph. It does not tell a full story, but it suggests one. What story might lie behind this 'word picture'?

■ The African American writer Langston Hughes also tells a story which might have been reported in the newspaper. His poem, *Ballad of the landlord* makes a protest, as does Peter Appleton's *The other time*. What are they protesting about?

■ *What has happened to Lulu?* suggests a situation, but does not give the details. We must imagine for ourselves who Lulu is, where she lives and what has happened to her.

■ The Bible contains one of the world's great collections of stories. Gareth Owen tells of Jonah's adventures with the whale in an unusual way. What feelings does Jonah have? (There are several.) Try bringing them out in a reading.

■ In *Ballad of the bread man* Charles Causley summarises the whole Christian story. What moral has he for his readers?

■ Why do poets try to re-tell such stories? Some people think it is irreverent to do this. What do you think?

Bezuidenhout

We rose.
The orderly pulled him to his feet.
The judge had said
'no extenuating circumstances' and 'no alternative'.
5 The sentence was read.
The boy's eyes sped
from judge to orderly
to his mother
in the gallery.

10 His brother had taken his bicycle
without his permission.
He had run down the dusty location road,
and stabbed him dead.

Now his body was jerking.
15 The orderly closed in.
The judge left the court
quite white in the face.
It had taken him two days
to understand the story
20 because they were country coloureds
and spoke Afrikaans differently
and witnesses contradicted each other.

His mother
leant over the gallery
25 and asked, 'Wat makeer?'
The orderly walked past,
drew his finger across his throat,
and said, 'Hy kry die tou.'

She rose,
30 silent and slowly it seemed,
her arms reaching out
in tattered coat sleeves,
threw her head back and screamed
NEE, NEE, HY'S MY KIND, MY LAASTE KIND.
35 EK HET NIE MEER KINDERS NIE!

Her husband stopped twisting his hat
'and dragged her out of court.

I used her words to start my newspaper report.
But now, eight years later, when I remember it,
40 I think above all of
not a terrified jerking face
not a scarecrow mother crucified
but of the orderly, Bezuidenhout,
dragging his finger across his own throat.

Damian Ruth *South Africa*

'Wat makeer?' (line 25): 'What's happening?'
(line 28): 'He gets the rope.'
(lines 34–5): 'No, no, he's my child, my last child. I have
no more children, none!'

The Lagos-Ibadan road before Shagamu

A bus groaned uphill. Trapped
In their seats, fifty-odd passengers rocked
To its pulse, each dreaming
Of a different destination.
5   GOD'S TIME IS THE BEST, read
One legend. NO CONDITION IS
PERMANENT, said another. And on,
On over the hill Shittu
Drove the lot, a cloud of Indian hemp
10 Unfolding among his robes. With
The swish over his shoulders, it
Trailed out, touched tails with the smoke
That squatted all indigo
On the hillside: like a stream
15 Was the going downhill, swift
Past recollection, straight into a bend
Upturned as a saucer, and
The journey spilt over in a ditch.
In the early morning sun,
20 To the clamour of flies that first
Answered the alarm, water
Of sewage kind washed their common
Wound, silenced their common groan.

NO NEED OF FIRST AID,
25 ALL DIED ON THE SPOT,
Said the dailies. THE POLICE,
WELL SUPPLIED WITH NOTES,
ARE LOOKING FOR THE DRIVER
WHO ESCAPED UNHURT.

John Pepper Clark *Nigeria*

Food for the couple

He hadn't gone to the wedding ceremony
at the local parish.
I asked him why.
'Man, it's my brother Sitha,' he started.
5 'He courted her for three years
They went steady for four years.
They quarrelled, he went to Jo'burg
And swore he didn't want her
There were brighter girls there –
10 What was she but an old maid?
Away he went for five years.
Until he heard she was marrying
this morning her former highschoolday teacher
– his arch rival.
15 He came back last night – almost greying all over.
And a damned stupid thing he did
this morning. He hanged himself
– in the lavatory.'

Mafika Gwala *South Africa*

One for the road

He came in
dusty sweaty redrimmed eyes
ordered a coke, downed it in one gulp,
picked up his bag with a woman's clothing in it
5 slung it over hunched shoulders
and turned to go –
It was then we noticed
the black band pinned on his coat sleeve ...

Charles Mungoshi *Zimbabwe*

What has happened to Lulu?

What has happened to Lulu, mother?
What has happened to Lu?
There's nothing in her bed but an old rag-doll
And by its side a shoe.

5 Why is her window wide, mother,
The curtain flapping free,
And only a circle on the dusty shelf
Where her money-box used to be?

Why do you turn your head, mother,
10 And why do the tear-drops fall?
And why do you crumple that note on the fire
And say it is nothing at all?

I woke to voices last night,
I heard an engine roar.
15 Why do you tell me the things I heard
Were a dream and nothing more?

I heard somebody cry, mother,
In anger or in pain,
But now I ask you why, mother,
20 You say it was a gust of rain.

Why do you wander about as though
You don't know what to do?
What has happened to Lulu, mother?
What has happened to Lu?

Charles Causley *England*

Ballad of the landlord

Landlord, landlord,
My roof has sprung a leak.
Don't you remember I told you about it
Way last week?

5 Landlord, landlord,
These steps is broken down.
When you come up yourself
It's a wonder you don't fall down.

Ten Bucks you say I owe you?
10 Ten Bucks you say is due?
Well, that's Ten Bucks more'n I'll pay you
Till you fix this house up new.

What? You gonna get eviction orders?
You gonna cut off my heat?
15 You gonna take my furniture and
Throw it in the street?

Um-huh! You talking high and mighty.
Talk on – till you get through.
You ain't gonna be able to say a word
20 If I land my fist on you.

Police! Police!
Come and get this man!
He's trying to ruin the government
And overturn the land!

25 Copper's whistle!
Patrol bell!
Arrest.
Precinct Station.
Iron cell.
30 Headlines in press:

MAN THREATENS LANDLORD

TENANT HELD NO BAIL

JUDGE GIVES NEGRO 90 DAYS IN COUNTY JAIL

Langston Hughes *U.S.A.*

The other time

He killed a man
In a drunken brawl;
They tried him, hanged him,
That was all.

5 But he left his wife
Nearly penniless,
She was raven-haired,
She was glamorous.

She had swooned in court,
10 She had caused a stir.
And the editor of
The *Sunday Blare*,

Aware of his readers'
Appetite
15 And judging she should
Be worth a bit,

Hurried a snooper
Round to her house
With an offer he thought
20 Quite fabulous

If she'd lend her picture,
Lend her name
To a story about
Her life with Him.

25 They'd write it up
From what she said.
Did she understand?
She understood.

'I never had much
30 I've still less now,
I need the money.
The answer's No.'

As he rose to go
He noticed a medal,
35 Mounted and framed,
Above the mantel.

And asked her about it.
Where was it won?
When did he get it?
40   What had he done?

'Oh, that,' she said.
'They pinned that on
The other time
He killed a man.'

Peter Appleton *England*

raven-haired (7): black-haired
snooper (17): here, a reporter from the
newspaper
mantel (36): shelf above the fireplace

Jonah and the whale

Well, to start with
It was dark
So dark
You couldn't see
5   Your hand in front of your face:
And huge
Huge as an acre of farm-land.

How do I know?
Well, I paced it out
10   Length and breadth
That's how.
And if you was to shout
You'd hear your own voice resound,
Bouncing along the ridges of its stomach,
15   Like when you call out
Under a bridge
Or, in an empty hall.

Hear anything?
No not much.
20 Only the normal
Kind of sounds
You'd expect to hear
Inside a whale's stomach;
The sea swishing far away,
25 Food gurgling, the wind
and suchlike sounds;
Then there was me screaming for help,
But who'd be likely to hear,
Us being miles from
30 Any shipping lines
And anyway
Supposing someone did hear,
Who'd think of looking inside a whale?
That's not the sort of thing
35 That people do.

Smell? I'll say there was a smell.
And cold. The wind blew in
Something terrible from the South
Each time he opened his mouth
40 Or took a swallow of some titbit.
The only way I found
To keep alive at all
Was to wrap my arms
Tight around myself
45 And race from wall to wall.

Damp? You can say that again:
When the ocean came sluicing in
I had to climb his ribs
To save myself from drowning.

50 Fibs? You think I'm telling you fibs,
I haven't told the half of it brother.
I'm only giving a modest account
Of what these two eyes have seen
And that's the truth on it.
55 Here, one thing I'll say
Before I'm done –
Catch me eating fish
From now on.

Gareth Owen *England*

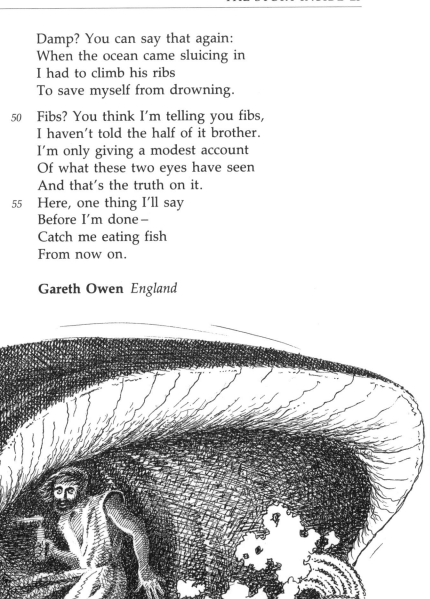

Ballad of the bread man

Mary stood in the kitchen
Baking a loaf of bread.
An angel flew in through the window.
We've a job for you, he said.

5 God in his big gold heaven,
Sitting in his big blue chair,
Wanted a mother for his little son.
Suddenly saw you there.

Mary shook and trembled,
10 It isn't true what you say.
Don't say that, said the angel.
The baby's on its way.

Joseph was in the workshop
Planing a piece of wood.
15 The old man's past it, the neighbours said
That girl's been up to no good.

And who was that elegant feller,
They said, in the shiny gear?
The things they said about Gabriel
20 Were hardly fit to bear.

Mary never answered,
Mary never replied.
She kept the information,
Like the baby, safe inside.

25 It was election winter.
They went to vote in town.
When Mary found her time had come
The hotels let her down.

The baby was born in an annex
30 Next to the local pub.
At midnight, a delegation
Turned up from the Farmers' Club.

They talked about an explosion
That cracked a hole in the sky,
35 Said they'd been sent to the *Lamb and Flag*
To see God come down from on high.

A few days later a bishop
And a five-star general were seen
With the head of an African country
40 In a bullet-proof limousine.

We've come, they said, with tokens
For the little boy to choose.
Told the tale about war and peace
In the television news.

45 After them came the soldiers
With rifle and bomb and gun,
Looking for enemies of the state.
The family had packed and gone.

When they got back to the village
50 The neighbours said, to a man,
That boy will never be one of us,
Though he does what he blessed well can.

He went round to all the people
A paper crown on his head.
55 Here is some bread from my father.
Take, eat, he said.

Nobody seemed very hungry.
Nobody seemed to care.
Nobody saw the god in himself
60 Quietly standing there.

He finished up in the papers.
He came to a very bad end.
He was charged with bringing the living to life.
No man was that prisoner's friend.

65 There's only one kind of punishment
To fit that kind of a crime.
They rigged a trial and shot him dead.
They were only just in time.

They lifted the young man by the leg,
70 They lifted him by the arm,
They locked him in a cathedral
In case he came to harm.

They stored him safe as water
Under seven rocks.
75 One Sunday morning he burst out
Like a jack-in-the-box.

Through the town he went walking.
He showed them the holes in his head.
Now do you want any loaves? he cried.
80 Not today, they said.

Charles Causley *England*

annex (29): room built onto a main building
Lamb and Flag (35): name of the inn, or public house
(pub), in the story
jack-in-the-box (76): toy doll fixed to a spring so that it
jumps out of its box when this is opened

Faces of love

Faces of love

Love of a mother for her child is one of the most powerful of human feelings. How does Kim Nam Jo convey these feelings in an unusual way? How do *Isatou died* and *Beloved of my mother* treat the loss of a child?

■ Eddison Zvobgo conveys tender feelings for a grandmother in his poem *Grandma at 90 o'clock*. But what wider, less personal feelings does he also express?

■ Sexual love is one of the most overpowering of feelings, but a feeling very difficult to define. Mervyn Morris uses comparisons in his attempt at a definition. How successful do you think he has been? There is also an unusual comparison in the poem on page 35. How can a person's life be a 'serenade' (line 20)? Which of the other love poems on pages 34 to 38 do you like. Can you say why?

■ Nearly two thousand years ago, the wife of the Chinese emperor and poet Wu-ti died. On page 39 are three translations of the poem he wrote to console him in his distress. Each translation presents the ideas of the original poem in a different way. Can you describe these differences? Which version do you prefer and why?

■ Love poems are generally more about courtship than marriage. Why might this be? What is Everett Standa's view of marriage? Would you say it is pessimistic – or honest and realistic?

■ The senryu is a traditional short Japanese poem. The modern senryu on page 41 all give glimpses of married life – suggesting more than they say. Can you think of stories suggested by each? Share your ideas.

■ What makes *Letter from a contract worker* such a moving poem? Practise reading it individually, to bring out its emotion.

My baby has no name yet

My baby has no name yet;
like a new-born chick or a puppy
my baby is not named yet.

What numberless texts I examined
5   at dawn and night and evening over again!
But not one character did I find
which is as lovely as the child.

Starry fields of the sky,
or heap of pearls in the depth.
10 Where can the name be found, how can I?

My baby has no name yet;
like an unnamed bluebird or white flowers
from the farthest land for the first,
I have no name for this baby of ours.

Kim Nam Jo *Korea*
Translated by Ko Won

character (6): a word, in decorated Chinese script.

Beloved of my mother

Beloved of my mother
        is like plucked vegetable leaves;
His large eyes are wide open,
His teeth are white like dry-season
        simsim;
5   Death has destroyed a prince,
Today, he is lost.
Son of the chief,
Beloved of my mother
Is like plucked vegetable leaves.

Okot p'Bitek *Uganda*

simsim (5): cooked maize

Isatou died

Isatou died
When she was only five
And full of pride
Just before she knew
5   How small a loss
It brought to such a few.
Her mother wept
Half grateful
To be so early bereft.
10   And did not see the smile
As tender as the root
Of the emerging plant
Which sealed her eyes.
The neighbours wailed
15   As they were paid to do
And thought how big a spread
Might be her wedding too.
The father looked at her
Through marble eyes and said;
20   'Who spilt the perfume
Mixed with morning dew?'

Lenrie Peters *The Gambia*

Grandma at 90 o'clock

... and now she remains –
knotted, gnarled and scarred:
survivor of myriad Nagasakis
up and down the corridors of time

5   she reclines
tenderly – a mere bundle
of ropes, thread-bare
for wear.

black soul;
10   her face a cartographer's nightmare,
strewn with contours and boulders –
a rugged terrain.

THE POETRY LIBRARY

those twinkling beads
encrusted in the shrunken skull
15 have beaten retreats to the trenches
till in sanctuaries said, 'no more.'

they have shed enough liquid
tokens now remain
in dewy clusters
20 dammed in little karibas

paved on the dreary cheeky terrain.
but, let the tongue unleash the computed data
long stored in recesses of memory;
then you drown in the African deluge.

25 tell-tales of black blood, rich red,
spilled over the dongas of battles won
and lost; or pain, hunger and disease;
of honour, custom and ancestral bonds;

of pride – never to fawn, bootlick or beg,
30 never to fall in love with chains once captive
nor to hide canines from foe
till you can descend on his texture and design.

now, she scans the horizon in puzzlement –
even beyond the blue to the Sea of Storms
35 like some ship-wrecked Admiral –
with neither medals nor pension.

Sleep, sleep now, jewel of Africa,
and absorb more of Africa's heat and moisture
Liberated and free from this 20th Century Egypt
40 amidst your peers beneath the wilderness.

Eddison Zvogbo *Zimbabwe*

Nagasakis: the city of Nagasaki in Japan, destroyed by
an atomic bomb in 1945
karibas (20): a reference to the Kariba dam on the
Zambia/Zimbabwe border
dongas (26): small valleys

Mama and daughter

Mama, please brush off my coat.
I'm going down the street.

Where're you going, daughter?

To see my sugar-sweet.

5 Who is your sugar, honey?
Turn around – I'll brush behind.

He is that young man, mama,
I can't get off my mind.

Daughter, once upon a time –
10 Let me brush the hem –
Your father, yes, he was the one!
I felt like that about him.

But it was a long time ago
He up and went his way.
15 I hope that wild young son-of-a-gun
Rots in hell today!

Mama, dad couldn't be still young.

He *was* young yesterday.
He *was* young when he –
20 Turn around!
So I can brush your back, I say!

Langston Hughes *U.S.A.*

Love is

a giving
and a measured taking

amputation
re-creating

5 everlasting
interface

a prison
and an open space

a teasing glimpse
10 of holy grail

a generator
that can fail

the naked jugular
the knife

15 the torsion
balance in my life

Mervyn Morris *Jamaica*

Two songs

O you whose eyes are painted, O girls,
You and the rifle – what you command is done.

I wish I could die for two days, then come back to life;
I should see, my lover, if your eyes would shed tears.

Berber, Western and Central Morocco

Serenade

Sing me a serenade,
a serenade about you.
Through your music talk to me,
let me understand you more.
5   Tell me about your pain,
about your sorrow.
Tell me about your happiness
and let me follow.
Let me see you as you are,
10   not as the world thinks you are.
I do not want to understand
what you show the world.
I want to know that real you,
that you in your song,
15   that innermost you that
you share with your song.
I want to understand you,
to understand your song.
Please, sing me the serenade,
20   the serenade of your life,
and maybe someday it might mingle,
might mingle with mine,
that our serenades together
might become as one.

Philippa Namutebi Barlow *Uganda*

The mesh

We have come to the crossroads
And I must either leave or come with you.
I lingered over the choice
5   But in the darkness of my doubts
You lifted the lamp of love
And I saw in your face
The road that I should take.

Kwesi Brew *Ghana*

The eyes that wouldn't wander

Yours were the eyes that wouldn't wander,
We met and parted like strangers,
Strangers who would not forget
But met again and again
5   As if by chance,
By passing each other and smiling
As though to someone else.

What was it that led us
Somewhere beyond
10   The eyes of the crowd
To a lonely spot
Where the eyes that wouldn't wander
Slowly rose and looked into mine?
What was this feeling
15   That raptured my nerves
As your trim fingers
Linked with mine?
What power lay hidden
In those eyes
20   That wouldn't wander?

Laban Erapu *Uganda*

The crack

Crack the glass,
And the crack
Will always remain.
The human heart
5 Has the same vein;
It's just as delicate
To the strain.

Once it is hurt,
It is too hard
10 To fade the stain.
Though parts can
Fix together –
You've just to touch the wound,
To make it drain again.

Sheikha El-Miskery *Oman*

Confession

i would
have brought
you
mulberries
5 but
they threatened
to explode
their mauve
corpuscles
10 all over
my
best shirt
so
i ate them

Christopher van Wyk *South Africa*

Like a flame

Raising up
from my weeding
of ripening cane

my eyes
5 make four
with this man

there ain't
no reason
to laugh

10 but
I laughing
in confusion

his hands
soft his words
15 quick his lips
curling as in
prayer

I nod

I like this man

20 Tonight
I go to meet him
like a flame

Grace Nichols *Guyana*

Mourning song (three translations)

The sound of rustling silk is stilled,
With dust the marble courtyard filled;
No footfalls echo on the floor,
Fallen leaves in heaps block up the door ...
5   For she, my pride, my lovely one, is lost,
And I am left, in hopeless anguish tossed.

H.A. Giles

The sound of her silk skirt has stopped.
On the marble pavement dust grows.
Her empty room is cold and still.
Fallen leaves are piled against the doors.
5   Longing for that lovely lady
How can I bring my aching heart to rest?

Arthur Waley

The rustling of silk is discontinued,
Dust drifts over the courtyard,
There is no sound of footfall, and the leaves
Scurry into heaps and lie still,
5   And she the rejoicer of the heart is beneath them:

A wet leaf that clings to the threshold.

Ezra Pound

Wedding eve

Should I
Or should I not
Take the oath to love
For ever
5 This person I know little about?

Does she love me
Or my car
Or my future
Which I know little about?

10 Will she continue to love me
When the future she saw in me
Crumbles and fades into nothing
Leaving the naked me
To love without hope?

15 Will that smile she wears
Last through the hazards to come
When fate strikes
Across the dreams of tomorrow?

Or will she,
20 Like the clever passenger in a faulty plane,
Wear her life jacket
And jump out to save her life
Leaving me to crash into the unknown?

What magic can I use
25 To see what lies beneath
Her angel face and well knit hair
To see her hopes and dreams
Before I take the oath
To love forever?

30 We are both wise chess players
She makes a move
I make a move
And we trap each other in our secret dreams
Hoping to win against each other.

Everett Standa *Kenya*

A senryu sequence

A father at last –
Like a lizard,
Stopping, starting, stopping.

In the beautiful woman,
5 Somewhere or other
His wife finds flaws.

Making it up –
To be the first to smile
Ashamed, it seems.

10 She suckles her baby:
'On the shelf
You'll find some sardines.'

After he's scolded
His wife too much,
15 He cooks the rice.

In the whole village
The husband alone
Does not know of it.

The morning after she's gone
20 He's very busy
Just finding everything.

Traditional, Japan

New face

I have learned not to worry about love;
but to honour its coming
with all my heart.
To examine the dark mysteries
5 of the blood
with headless heed and
swirl,
to know the rush of feelings
swift and flowing
10 as water.
The source appears to be
some inexhaustible
spring
within our twin and triple
15 selves;
the new face I turn up
to you
no one else on earth
has ever
20 seen.

Alice Walker *U.S.A.*

Letter from a contract worker

I wanted to write you a letter
my love
a letter to tell
of this longing
5   to see you
and this fear
of losing you
of this thing which deeper than I want, I feel
a nameless pain which pursues me
10 a sorrow wrapped about my life.

I wanted to write you a letter
my love
a letter of intimate secrets
a letter of memories of you
15 of you
your lips as red as the *tacula* fruit
your hair black as the dark *diloa* fish
your eyes gentle as the *macongue*
your breasts firm as young *moboque* fruit
20 your light walk
your caresses
better than any I find down here.

I wanted to write you a letter
my love
25 to bring back our days together in our secret haunts
nights lost in the long grass
to bring back the shadow of your legs
and the moonlight filtering through the endless
palms,
30 to bring back the madness of our passion
and the bitterness of separation.

I wanted to write you a letter
my love
which you could not read without crying
35 which you would hide from your father Bombo
and conceal from your mother Kieza
which you would read without the indifference
of forgetfulness,

a letter which would make any other
40 in all Kilombo worthless.

I wanted to write you a letter
my love)
a letter which the passing wind would take
a letter which the cashew and the coffee trees,
45 the hyenas and the buffalo,
the caymens and the river fish
could hear
the plants and the animals
pitying our sharp sorrow
50 from song to song
lament to lament
breath to caught breath
would leave to you, pure and hot,
the burning
55 the sorrowful words of the letter
I wanted to write to you

I wanted to write you a letter
But my love, I don't know why it is,
why, why, why it is, my love,
60 but you can't read
and I–oh the hopelessness–I can't write.

Antonio Jacinto *Angola*

Working days

Working days

Some people look on work as only a necessary evil, so many hours spent each week just to earn a wage to live on. But the first poet in this section sees work in a more positive way. Or do you think this view is too idealistic? Certainly, the palm-wine tapper is enjoying his work in the second poem. The reapers in the mieliefield and the girls planting rice seem rather less joyful. Why might this be so? What is the particular pain of the contract worker?

- In the extract from *Islands* we get two views of work. What are they? How does the driver also see his work in more than one way in *Song of the wagon driver*?

- The poems on pages 53 to 54 show women at work. What particular problems of women's work do they suggest? Do they give a balanced view?

However unpleasant some types of work are it can be much worse to need work and not to be able to find it. In *Hunting for a job* we have a picture of a desperate job-seeker. What story might lie behind this poem?

Work

There is no point in work
unless it absorbs you
like an absorbing game

If it doesn't absorb you
5   if it's never any fun,
don't do it.

When a man goes out into his work
he is alive like a tree in spring,
he is living, not merely working.

D.H. Lawrence *England*

The palm-wine tapper's song

Like the bat I dance
The dance of the heights,
Only I
Can sing this morning song –
5   In the roof of the one-pole hut:
Virgin secretion,
The dim white ooze of the firm one,
Result of last night's assault,
Only for you I dare it:
10   Tamed the ugly giant,
Punctuated his fibrous age-height
With craggy footsteps,
Thrust at his sinewy neck
Rope-balance beyond the reach of the 'gunnuko.
15   Earth-bound ones lick the cow's underside;
I am not dizzy,
I hug the erect crocodile, suck
Its wounded neck up in birds' heights.
My brethren's ways are terrain,
20   They are level, wide and long, but low.
Mine are upright, narrow – but high.
Proud spirit that flows upwards,
I am come to meet you at climb climax.
The first drop down to the up-lookers,
25   Open-jawed spirits of earth.
The next drop down into my stomach:
Wet my throat and talk to me –
Not my sole, I dread a downward hurry –
Neither my head, don't push me below.
30   This last tilt into the tame pour,
For others must know your ecstasy
Only in watery fragments.

Segun Sofowote *Nigeria*

'gunnuko (14): Traditional masquerades, some of which
can be very frightening

Reapers in a mieliefield

Faces furrowed and wet with sweat,
Bags tied to their wasp waists,
women reapers bend mielie stalks,
break cobs in rustling sheaths,
5   toss them in the bags
and move through row upon row of maize.

Behind them, like a desert tanker,
a dust-raising tractor
pulls a trailer,
10   driven by a pipe-puffing man
flashing tobacco-stained teeth
as yellow as the harvested grain.

He stops to pick up bags
loaded by thick-limbed labourers
15   in vests baked
brown with dust.

The sun lashes
the workers with
a red-hot rod;
29   they stop for a while
to wipe a brine-bathed brow
and drink from battered cans
bubbling with malty *maheu.*

Thirst is slaked in seconds,
25   Men jerk bags like feather cushions
and women become prancing wild mares;
soon the day's work will be done
and the reapers will rest in their kraals.

Mbuyiseni Oswald Mtshali *South Africa*

mielie (3): maize
maheu (23): mielie meal gruel, slightly fermented
and drunk cold
kraal (28): village

Paddy rice song

Girls planting paddy:
Only their song
Free of the mud.

Konishi Raizan *Japan*

Song of agony

I put on a clean shirt
and go to work my contract
   Which of us
   Which of us will come back?
5   Four and twenty moons
not seeing women
not seeing my ox
not seeing my land
   Which of us
10   Which of us will die?
I put on a clean shirt
and go to work my contract
to work far away
I go beyond the mountain
15   into the bush
where the road ends
and the river runs dry.
   Which of us
   Which of us will come back?
20   Which of us
   Which of us will die?

Gouveia de Lemos *Angola*

from Islands

My uncle made chairs, tables, balanced doors on, dug out
coffins, smoothing the white wood out

with plane and quick sandpaper until
it shone like his short-sighted glasses.

5 The knuckles of his hands were sil-
vered knobs of nails hit, hurt and flat-

tened out with the blast of a heavy hammer. He was knock-
knee'd, flat-
footed and his clip clop sandals slapped across the concrete

flooring of his little shop where canefield mulemen and a fleet
10 of Bedford lorry drivers dropped in to scratch themselves and
talk.

There was no shock of wood, no beam
of light mahogany his saw teeth couldn't handle.

When shaping squares for locks, a key hole
care tapped rat tat tat upon the handle

15 of his humpbacked chisel. Cold
world of wood caught fire as he whittled: rectangle

window frames, the intersecting x of fold-
ing chairs, triangle

trellises, the donkey
20 box-cart in its squeaking square.

But he was poor and most days he was hungry.
Imported cabinets with mirrors, formica table

tops, spine-curving chairs made up of tubes, with hollow
steel-like bird bones that sat on rubber ploughs,

25 thin beds, stretched not on boards, but blue high-tensioned
cables,
were what the world preferred.

And yet he had a block of wood that would have baffled them.
With knife and gimlet care he worked away at this on Sundays,

explored its knotted hurts, cutting his way
30 along its yellow whorls until his hands could feel

how it swelled and shivered, breathing air,
its weathered green burning to rings of time,

its contoured grain still tuned to roots and water.
And as he cut, he heard the creak of forests:

35 green lizard faces gulped, grey memories with moth
eyes watched him from their shadows, soft

liquid tendrils leaked among their flowers
and a black rigid thunder he had never heard within his hammer

came stomping up the trunks. And as he worked within his
shattered
40 Sunday shop, the wood took shape: dry shuttered

eyes, slack anciently everted lips, flat
ruined face, eaten by pox, ravaged by rat

and woodworm, dry cistern mouth, cracked
gullet crying for the desert, the heavy black

45 enduring jaw; lost pain, lost iron;
emerging woodwork image of his anger.

Edward Kamau Brathwaite *Barbados*

whorls (30): rings in the wood
everted (41): turned outwards (rarely-used)
pox (42): smallpox

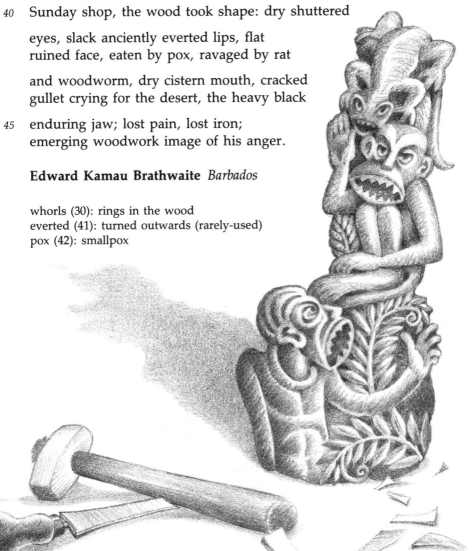

Song of the wagondriver

My first love was the ten-ton truck
They gave me when I started,
And though she played the bitch with me
I grieved when we were parted.

5 Since then I've had a dozen more,
The wound was quick to heal,
And now it's easier to say
I'm married to my wheel.

I've trunked it north, I've trunked it south,
10 On wagons good and bad,
But none was ever really like
The first I ever had.

The life is hard, the hours are long,
Sometimes I cease to feel,
15 But I go on, for it seems to me
I'm married to my wheel.

Often I think of my home and kids,
Out on the road at night,
And think of taking a local job
20 Provided the money's right.

Two nights a week I see my wife,
And eat a decent meal,
But otherwise, for all my life,
I'm married to my wheel.

B.S. Johnson *England*

trunked (9): travelling along a trunk (main) road;
the poet has made up this word; it is not part of
standard English

Woman work

I've got the children to tend
The clothes to mend
The floor to mop
The food to shop
5   Then the chicken to fry
The baby to dry
I got company to feed
The garden to weed
I've got the shirts to press
10   The tots to dress
The cane to be cut
I gotta clean up this hut
Then see about the sick
And the cotton to pick.

15   Shine on me, sunshine
Rain on me, rain
Fall softly, dewdrops
And cool my brow again.

THE POETRY LIBRARY

Storm, blow me from here
20 With your fiercest wind
Let me float across the sky
'Til I can rest again.

Fall gently, snowflakes
Cover me with white

25 Cold icy kisses and
Let me rest tonight.

Sun, rain, curving sky
Mountain, oceans, leaf and stone
Star shine, moon glow
30 You're all that I can call my own.

Maya Angelou *U.S.A.*

Career woman

Thirty-five and very plain
she is learning to settle down
to her underpaid job as clerk-typist
in some obscure firm of lawyers in the city.

5 Slowly, she is learning to
wrap her dreams like a hot-water bottle
round her few belongings in her little room
that demands over half her wages in Southerton.

Thirty-five and childless
10 she is painfully coming to terms with reality
quietly sinking down into the centre
of her age's demands and limitations.

Like some aquatic thing
in the middle of a puddle
15 at the beginning of a very long
dry season.

Charles Mungoshi *Zimbabwe*

Southerton (8): suburb of Zimbabwe's capital city, Harare

Daydream

dear sir
with reference
to yours of the
taste
5 of your mouth
lingers in
mine
laughing
tongues noses lips
10 eye
lashes oh!
exc
use me Sir
23rd
15 inst . . .

Jeannette Leboent Kassam *Kenya*

The woman I married

The woman I married
is an outright bone-shaker.
For a full decade
She had banged a typewriter
5 And now in substitution
Bangs the crockery
Until my house sounds like a factory.

The noise keeps her sane,
They say.

Edwin Waiyaki *Kenya*

Hunting for a job

Seeing him,
Strolling from somewhere,
To nowhere
He would have convinced you
5   He was an ordinary young man,
In ordinary circumstances.

But,
If you looked closer,
You might have noticed:
10   The frayed high collar,
And the smudgy-looking face
And,
If you had peered beneath his coat
You would have seen:
15   The clean collar
Attached to a sleeveless rag,
That was no shirt.
If you could have examined,
The soles of his shoes,
20   You would have discovered:
Two gaping holes there
And a pair of drenched socks,
Coming through.
There is an air about him,
25   As of a young man,
Who knew how to wear his clothes.
One must appear so
If one is hunting for a job.

Elias Nyakunu *Zimbabwe*

The price of freedom

The price of freedom

Freedom is often seen as something lost, or as a political struggle still to be won. In many parts of the world, writers have been imprisoned for writing what they felt about freedom – or the lack of it – in their own society. Poems, songs and plays have been banned, and writers forced into exile because people listened to them. There are many different kinds of freedom, as the poems in this section illustrate.

- *Colonizer's logic* sums up the attitude of many who robbed Africa of its freedom in the past. How does Chinweizu make his point?

- How would you describe the ending of the poem *Stanley meets Mutesa* where David Rubadiri looks back on a carefully-chosen moment in African history?

- *The weaver bird* illustrates the effect of colonialism on Africa. Can you work out in detail what Kofi Awoonor means at each stage of the poem? *The making of a servant* has a similar message.

- *There was an Indian* describes another fateful meeting of cultures – the arrival of Columbus in America in 1492. Many native Americans were later killed or enslaved by the Europeans. During the following centuries, further millions of men, women and children were transported from Africa to work on the American plantations. What does Maya Angelou say about their story and hers in *Still I rise*?

- The poems on pages 66 to 75 are all reminders of the hardships and sacrifices made in the struggle for freedom. *The laying of stones* is a wonderful poem to read aloud. How might this be done most effectively?

- The final poem in this section reminds us that many who are poor or weak still suffer at the hands of those who are more powerful. What do you think Marjorie Macgoye feels about Atieno? Why has she called the poem *Freedom song*?

Colonizer's logic

These natives are unintelligent –
We can't understand their language.

Chinweizu *Nigeria*

Stanley meets Mutesa

Such a time of it they had;
The heat of the day,
The chill of the night
And the mosquitoes that followed.
5 Such was the time and
They bound for a kingdom.

The thin weary line of carriers
With tattered dirty rags to cover their backs;
The battered bulky chests
10 That kept on falling off their shaven heads.
Their tempers high and hot,
The sun fierce and scorching –
With it rose their spirits,
With its fall their hopes
15 As each day sweated their bodies dry and
Flies clung in clumps on their sweat-scented backs.
Such was the march
And the hot season just breaking.

Each day a weary pony dropped,
20 Left for the vultures on the plains;
Each afternoon a human skeleton collapsed,
Left for the Masai on the plains;
But the march trudged on
Its Khaki leader in front;
25 He the spirit that inspired.
He the light of hope.

Then came the afternoon of a hungry march,
A hot and hungry march it was;
The Nile and the Nyanza
30 Lay like two twins
Azure across the green countryside.
The march leapt on chaunting
Like young gazelles to a water hole.
Hearts beat faster,
35 Loads felt lighter
As the cool water lapped their sore soft feet.
No more the dread of hungry hyenas
But only tales of valour when
At Mutesa's court fires are lit.

40 No more the burning heat of the day
But song, laughter and dance.

The village looks on behind banana groves,
Children peer behind reed fences.
Such was the welcome.
45 No singing women to chaunt a welcome
Or drums to greet the white ambassador;
Only a few silent nods from aged faces
And one rumbling drum roll
To summon Mutesa's court to parley
50 For the country was not sure.

The gate of reeds is flung open,
There is silence
But only a moment's silence –
A silence of assessment.
55 The tall black king steps forward,
He towers over the thin bearded white man
Then grabbing his lean white hand
Manages to whisper
'Mtu Mweupe karibu'
60 White man you are welcome.
The gate of polished reed closes behind them
And the west is let in.

David Rubadiri *Malawi*

chaunt (32 and 45): chant

The weaver bird

The weaver bird built in our house
And laid its eggs on our only tree
We did not want to send it away
We watched the building of the nest
5 And supervised the egg-laying.
And the weaver returned in the guise of the owner
Preaching salvation to us that owned the house
They say it came from the west
Where the storms at sea had felled the gulls
10 And the fishers dried their nets by lantern light
Its sermon is the divination of ourselves
And our new horizons limit as its nest
But we cannot join the prayers and answers of the communicants.
We look for new homes every day,
15 For new altars we strive to re-build
The old shrines defiled from the weaver's excrement.

Kofi Awoonor *Ghana*

The making of a servant

I can no longer ask how it feels
To be choked by a yoke-rope
Because I have seen it for myself in the chained ox.
The blindness has left my eyes. I have become aware,
5 *I have seen the making of a servant*
In the young yoke-ox.

He was sleek, born for freedom,
Not asking anything from anyone, simply
priding himself on being a young ox.
10 Someone said: Let him be caught and
trained and broken in.
Going about it as if he meant to help him.
I have seen the making of a servant
In the young yoke-ox.

15   He tried to resist, fighting for his freedom.
He was surrounded, fenced in with wisdom and experience.
They overcame him by trickery: 'He must be trained.'
A good piece of rationalisation can camouflage evil.
I have seen the making of a servant
20   *In the young yoke-ox.*

He was bound with ropes that cut into his head,
He was bullied, kicked, now and again petted,
But their aim was the same: to put a yoke on him.
Being trained in one's own interests is for the privileged.
25   *I have seen the making of a servant*
In the young yoke-ox.

The last stage. The yoke is set on him.
They tie the halter round his neck, slightly choking him.
They say the job's done, he'll be put to work with
   the others
30   To obey the will of his owner and taskmaster.
I have seen the making of a servant
In the young yoke-ox.

He kicks out, trying to break away.
They speak with their whips. He turns backwards
35   Doing his best to resist but then they say: 'Hit him.'
A prisoner is a coward's plaything.
I have seen the making of a servant
In the young yoke-ox.

J.J.R. Jolobe *South Africa*
Translated from the Xhosa by R. Kavanagh *and* Z. Quangulem

There was an Indian

There was an Indian, who had known no change,
Who strayed content along a sunlit beach
Gathering shells. He heard a sudden strange
Commingled noise; looked up; and gasped for speech.
5 For in the bay, where nothing was before,
Moved on the sea, by magic, huge canoes,
With bellying cloths on poles, and not one oar,
And fluttering coloured signs, and clambering crews.
And he, in his fear, this naked man alone,
10 His fallen hands forgetting all their shells,
His lips gone pale, knelt low behind a stone
And stared, and saw, and did not understand,
Columbus's doom-burdened caravels
Slant to the shore, and all their seamen land.

John Squires *England*

caravels (13): light, fast sailing-ships

Still I rise

You may write me down in history
With your bitter, twisted lies,
You may tread me in the very dirt
But still, like dust, I'll rise.

5 Does my sassiness upset you?
Why are you beset with gloom?
'Cause I walk like I've got oil wells
Pumping in my living room.

Just like moons and like suns,
10 With the certainty of tides,
Just like hopes springing high,
Still I'll rise.

Did you want to see me broken?
Bowed head and lowered eyes?
15 Shoulders falling down like teardrops,
Weakened by my soulful cries.

Does my haughtiness offend you?
Don't you take it awful hard?
'Cause I laugh like I've got gold mines
20 Diggin' in my own back yard.

You may shoot me with your words,
You may cut me with your eyes,
You may kill me with your hatefulness,
But still, like air, I'll rise.

25 Does my sexiness upset you?
Does it come as a surprise?
That I dance like I've got diamonds
At the meeting of my thighs?

Out of the huts of history's shame
30 I rise
Up from a past that's rooted in pain
I rise
I'm a black ocean, leaping and wide,
Welling and swelling I bear in the tide.

35 Leaving behind nights of terror and fear
    I rise
    Into a daybreak that's wondrously clear
    I rise
    Bringing the gifts that my ancestors gave,
70 I am the dream and the hope of the slave.
    I rise
    I rise
    I rise.

Maya Angelou *U.S.A.*

sassiness (5): defiance

To Mai
(from Prison Letters)

Dear Mai,
as long as I can still cough and spit
as long as I can still hold this pen
I am alive, Mai.
5   I hope you are well also.
Please do not let your mind fill with darkness
do not gnaw your heart away with grief
I am alive, Mai,
it will be over before long.

10 Calm your heart, mother,
do not trouble yourself
that you cannot come to see your lost son.
I am not in the leopard's mouth
as you said in your last letter.

15 You came into my face last night,
so comforting you were
that I awoke with a feeling
that I should come to your hut to say
an early 'Morning, Mai.'

20 Please, tell little Ruth
to stop crying. Poor child,
What does she know?
A pity she should think I am dead.
Baba shouldn't have said it so straight
25 in her presence.
I am glad you have a comforter
in the Reverend's wife. My friend, her son,
is still in indefinite detention. So,
as the song goes, 'It's not I alone
30 who has trouble.'

I long for pumpkins
cooked in the same clay-pot with round nuts.
Preserve me some, Mai. Greetings to all the small ones.
I am your puking child,
35 Musaemura.

Musaemura Bonas Zimunya *Zimbabwe*

Touch

When I get out
I'm going to ask someone
  to touch me
  very gently please
5 and slowly,
  touch me
  I want
  to learn again
  how life feels.

10 I've not been touched
for seven years
  for seven years
  I've been untouched
  out of touch
15 and I've learnt
  to know now
  the meaning of
  untouchable.

Untouched – not quite
20 I can count the things
that have touched me

One: fists
At the beginning
  fierce mad fists
25 beating beating
  till I remember
  screaming
  don't touch me
  please don't touch me.

30 Two: paws
The first four years of paws
  every day
  patting paws, searching
  – arms up, shoes off
35 legs apart –
  prodding paws, systematic
  heavy, indifferent
  probing away
  all privacy.

40   I don't want fists and paws
I want
   to want to be touched
   again
   and to touch.
45   I want to feel alive
   again
   I want to say
   when I get out
Here I am
50   please touch me.

Hugh Lewin *South Africa*

from Letters to Martha

I remember rising one night
after midnight
and moving
through an impulse of loneliness
5   to try and find the stars.

And through the haze
the battens of fluorescents made
I saw pinpricks of white
I thought were stars.

10   Greatly daring
I thrust my arm through the bars
and easing the switch in the corridor
plunged my cell in darkness

I scampered to the window
15   and saw the splashes of light
where the stars flowered.

But through my delight
thudded the anxious boots
and a warning barked
20   from the machine-gun post
on the catwalk.

And it is the brusque inquiry
and threat
that I remember that night
25   rather than the stars.

Dennis Brutus *South Africa*

battens (7): strips of wood, carrying
electric lights

Another day *(For Bram Fischer)*

It was like any other day
from un-lock
  breakfast/wash-up/scrub/clean
  garden/lunch
5 lock-up
  wash-up/scrub-clean
  shower/4 o'clock supper
  lock-up
till un-lock next morning
10 any day every day
14 hour lock-up
every night

In the morning
we picked our 11 mielies
15 10 for us and 1 for the boer
which passed half an hour
and another half-hour passed
tearing off the husks

excited about our own-grown mielies
20 which we sent to be cooked for supper.
In the afternoon
we trimmed the 21 tomato bushes
and were pleased to see
how they were springing up
25 green with fruitfulness.

It was like any other day
  garden/lunch
  lock-up
  wash-up/scrub/clean
30 shower/4 o'clock supper
but just before supper
he was called
unexpectedly
for a visit
35 which means I said
  either something good
  or something bad
So he missed supper with us
and we took his mielie to his cell

40 to eat after his visit
    either something good
    or something bad

It was like any other day
    supper/lock-up
45 alone
    cell alone
    for 14 hours

While we ate
he was in the room
50 where you peer at your visitors
through a 4 inch strip of perspex
boxed in by wood panels
with sound-boards
to make the tapes clear.
55 You have boere on your side
they have boere on their side.

They call it the visitors room
His brother
peering through the perspex
60 into the wooden box
told him:
    Your son died this morning
through the perspex
into the wooden box
65 keeping the State secure
    Your son died this morning.

His supper I suppose was cold
by the time he got back to his cell
    alone
70 after lock-up
    for the next 14 hours
    like any other day.

Hugh Lewin *South Africa*

Bram Fischer was a leader of the South
African Communist Party. He died in 1976
while serving a life sentence.

boer (15): Afrikaner farmer, here used to refer
to their Afrikaner jailers in the prison

In detention

He fell from the ninth floor
He hanged himself
He slipped on a piece of soap while washing
He hanged himself
5 He slipped on a piece of soap while washing
He fell from the ninth floor
He hanged himself while washing
He slipped from the ninth floor
He hung from the ninth floor
10 He slipped on the ninth floor while washing
He fell from a piece of soap while slipping
He hung from the ninth floor
He washed from the ninth floor while slipping
He hung from a piece of soap while washing

Christopher van Wyk *South Africa*

The laying of the stones

They were children, remember?
They'd heard the call of the Ancestors
'The parasites must be destroyed,
For they've brought death into the land!'

5   Then Ngqika rose in them
    and gave them courage

Then Makhanda rose in them
    and gave them courage

Then Shaka rose in them
10   and gave them courage

Then Dingane rose in them
    and gave them courage

Then Moshoeshoe rose in them
    and gave them courage

15   Then Khama rose in them
    and gave them courage

See how the graves have risen
    and fired the children
    to new and unknown heights of courage

20   Let us remember them
Let us remember the children in the moment of their
greater glory –

Lay a stone here
    for the head of a child rests in this place

25   Lay a stone here
    for the head of a child rests in this place

Lay a stone here
    for the head of a child rests in this place

Daniel P. Kunene *South Africa*

The newest bride

They came in hordes singing her name,
Voices grew hoarse praising her beauty,
Her charm was beyond all compare,
Her soft touch soothed all pain,
5 Her words taught all wisdom,
And her embrace brought eternal bliss.

Moved to fever pitch I swore,
I swore before the gathered village,
I swore on the bones of my forefathers,
10 That I would neither sleep nor rest,
Until she was my wife, my betrothed.

It was a fever, as virulent a fever as you ever saw,
For I ask you my friends, my brothers,
Know you of any fool,
15 Who paid the bride price I paid,
Not ever having set eyes on the girl?

And what a bride price!
Facing Greener guns with stones,
Long prison sentences without trial,
20 Hunger strikes, deportation, the lot!
But I paid, I paid every cent of it.

At last she came, she came my bride!
The drums throbbed, they throbbed for a week,
The village sung and drunk,
25 We danced and laughed,
And drunk and laughed and danced again.

She was beautiful beyond compare,
Her sparkling eyes,
Her firm warm breasts,
30 Her beautiful smile and merry laughter,
Spelt beauty and joy for ever.

When I touched her hand,
Currents raced tingling through me,
I kissed her,
35 All was oblivion but those lips,
Oh! She was so beautiful.

But alas! Alas, my friends,
Time, that tireless teacher,
Time, the insatiable killer of joy,
40 And patient healer of all fevers,
Showed my bride was a woman.

Alas she is a woman,
A woman like my other wives,
Why can't she be my bride?
45 Why must she be like the others?
Must she join the harem?

Her eyes no longer speak love,
Only contempt when I rest.
Her words only harass me to work,
50 Her thoughts are problems,
Gone is my leisure, only worry remains.

Must I toil and sweat harder,
So our children can read?
Must I raise my voice in anger,
55 And sharpen my arrow and spears,
So my rich neighbours around
May not snatch her from me?

Must I forfeit my treasured leisure,
Must I spend sleepless nights,
60 Must my flying hours of youth
Be spent in cold calculating thought,
Must I age before my years,
So we can compare our home to others?

Oh that I could divorce you,
65 But God forbid! How could I say so?
Oh, Uhuru, my love, my sweet,
You are my bane, my life,
I love and hate you,
Your clutch is unrelenting.

70 Uhuru is my love, my Freedom.

Henry Barlow *Uganda*

Greener guns (18): High-quality type of rifle
Uhuru (66): Swahili word for freedom

THE POETRY LIBRARY

A freedom song

Atieno washes dishes,
Atieno plucks the chicken,
Atieno gets up early,
Beds her sack down in the kitchen,
5 Atieno eight years old,
Atieno yo.

Since she is my sister's child
Atieno needs no pay,
While she works my wife can sit
10 Sewing every sunny day:
With her earnings I support
Atieno yo.

Atieno's sly and jealous,
Bad example to the kids
15 Since she minds them, like a schoolgirl
Wants their dresses, shoes and beads,
Atieno ten years old,
Atieno yo.

Now my wife has gone to study
20 Atieno is less free.
Don't I keep her, school my own ones,
Pay the party, union fee,
All for progress: aren't you grateful
Atieno yo?

25 Visitors need much attention,
All the more when I work at night.
That girl spends too long at the market,
Who will teach her what is right?
Atieno rising fourteen,
30 Atieno yo.

Atieno's had a baby
So we know that she is bad.
Fifty fifty it may live
And repeat the life she had
35 Ending in post-partum bleeding,
Atieno yo.

Atieno's soon replaced.
Meat and sugar more than all
She ate in such narrow life
40 Were lavished on her funeral.
Atieno's gone to glory,
Atieno yo.

Marjorie Oludhe Macgoye *Kenya*

Modern living

Modern living

In *What's wrong with people?* Mongane Serote reminds us that today, as in the past, we are still responsible for one another. Perhaps things were better, in earlier societies? The first two poems examine this question.

- Ask your parents, grandparents and other relations what they think. Ask them for particular examples of changes they think have been for the worse. Have there been improvements, though?

- Why has Jared Angira laid out his poem as he has (page 84)? What impressions is he trying to give of city life?

- What impressions of the city are conveyed in the poems on pages 84 to 87? Do you share these points of view in any way? What in your opinion are the good and bad things about life in the country as against life in the city?

- Oumar Ba and Freddy Macha condemn public corruption in different ways in their poems on pages 88 and 89. How do they see the problem?

- Do you think Cecil Rajendra's view of so-called 'underdevelopment' is realistic in his poem on page 90?

- In this extract from *Song of Ocol*, Okot p'Bitek illustrates some of the divisions within a newly independent country. Who do you think he is criticising in the poem?

- The last poem in this section paints a picture of an individual who has become a loser in the modern city. Discuss the background to the story.

What's wrong with people?

I saw a man
Come. Walk. Limp,
Fall.
Like a branch being sawn.

5 His eyes flickered like flame blown by wild wind.

People stood to look.
I was among them.

Mongane Serote *South Africa*

Once upon a time

Once upon a time, son,
they used to laugh with their hearts
and laugh with their eyes;
but now they only laugh with their teeth,
5 while their ice-block-cold eyes
search behind my shadow.

There was a time indeed
they used to shake hands with their hearts;
but that's gone, son.
10 Now they shake hands without hearts
while their left hands search
my empty pockets.

'Feel at home'! 'Come again';
they say, and when I come
15 again and feel
at home, once, twice,
there will be no thrice –
for then I find doors shut on me.

So I have learned many things, son.
20 I have learned to wear many faces
like dresses – homeface,
officeface, streetface, hostface,
cocktailface, with all their conforming smiles
like a fixed portrait smile.

25 And I have learned, too,
to laugh with only my teeth
and shake hands without my heart.
I have also learned to say, 'Goodbye',
when I mean, 'Good-riddance';
30 to say, 'Glad to meet you',
without being glad; and to say 'It's been
nice talking to you', after being bored.

But believe me, son.
I want to be what I used to be
35 when I was like you. I want
to unlearn all these muting things.
Most of all, I want to relearn
how to laugh, for my laugh in the mirror
shows only my teeth like a snake's bare fangs!

40 So show me, son,
how to laugh; show me how
I used to laugh and smile
once upon a time when I was like you.

Gabriel Imomotime Okara *Nigeria*

African dancing

Where are the old men and the old women?
Dead, are they?
Those old savage dancers!
Half-naked, half-mad, and a quarter drunk!
5   At the beginning beer was brought but not drunk.
After a long time it was all finished.
They were great drunkards but bound by custom.
Today it has all gone – destroyed!
Our grandparents jive, rock and twist!
10   What can we do?
Look for skins, drums, feathers and ropes?
My grandmother is a specialist,
A dancer who can leap six feet.
What can amuse us more than this?
15   This cruel, physical, savage dancing –
There is no more of it today.
We now drink orange juice and forget.
Our muscles, brain and blood cry for our own dancing.
I remember five girls whom I saw –
20   Their breasts hanging towards the ground,
Their backs well-oiled with milk-fat,
Their feet anointed and of sweet colour.
My eyes never changed direction.
That was African dancing!
25   Where are the drums and the drummers?
Where are the huge clay pots of beer?
Where are the beautifully decorated faces of the women?
Can we let all these things pass?
30   I shall not. I am in need of them.
I am shy to tell my friends that I love them.
May the spirits on mountains descend.
We are thirsty for dancing and drinking.
We are your sons and your daughters.
35   Come upon us and heal the dying tradition –
The dying tribal dancing of you, our first forefathers!

Eric Mazani *Zimbabwe*

The street

Worms crawling   Worms crawling
            mercedes slides past
                blue shadow

                    garbage

5   swinging   swinging
               boozing   boozing

                zephyr slides past
                green shadow

        Wananchi   Wananchi

10   scratch
                    scratch
                    tiny nails
                    blocked nostrils

    vultures whirr   vultures whirr

15   The band splashes
                up the night-club

                    rolls-royce
                sleek and cool
                grey shadow

20   fireworks
                    diwali
                    warning light

    by shops   by shops

25   'closing down sale'
                non-citizen
                gloom shadow

                        mercedes
            trinity   mansion   trinity
                        shamba

30   and the street is clean
                the street is clean

Jared Angira *Kenya*

zephyr (7): like 'mercedes; and 'rolls-royce', a type of
motor car
Wananchi (9): the people
diwali (21): Hindu festival

An abandoned bundle

The morning mist
and chimney smoke
of White City Jabavu
5 flowed thick yellow
as pus oozing
from a gigantic sore.

It smothered our little houses
like fish caught in a net.

Scavenging dogs
10 draped in red bandanas of blood
fought fiercely
for a squirming bundle.

I threw a brick:
they bared fangs
15 flicked velvet tongues of scarlet
and scurried away,
leaving a mutilated corpse –
an infant dumped on a rubbish heap –
'Oh! Baby in the Manger
20 sleep well
on human dung.'

Its mother
had melted into the rays of the rising sun,
her face glittering with innocence
25 her heart as pure as untrampled dew.

Mbuyiseni Oswald Mtshali *South Africa*

White City Jabavu (3): name of a poor township in South
Africa

Neon

neon flashes in our skies
at night for boac
fiat and other gods –
we say look
5 how pretty
and open our arms
to embrace their promise

in the morning
when the harsh sun has
10 torn away the darkness
as if a whore had stripped
off a wig to reveal
her bald pate
we look at the ground and say
15 there is no rice in the shops

Amin Kassam *Kenya*

boac (2): stands for British Overseas Airways
Corporation (now British Airways)
pate (13): top of the head

Lost friends

They are imprisoned
In dark suits and air-conditioned offices
Alsatians ready at the door
On the saliva carpeted floor

5 They spend their nights
In jet airlines –
Would change them in mid-air
To show how much they dare

Drunk from the vertigo
10 Of never catching their tails
they never seem to know
When not to bite their nails

Their new addiction
Fortifies their livers
15 They are getting there
While the going's good
They have no time for dreamers.

Lenrie Peters *The Gambia*

vertigo (9): dizziness

Justice is done

Beaten up,
Robbed,
Hospitalised?
And the witnesses?
5 Many as grains of the sand:
Kadiel is one:
Ndoulla
Ndyam Bele is one
Even the birds can testify ...
10 But you forget that the chief
Has his son as the judge
And his son-in-law as interpreter.

Oumar Ba *Mauritania*

Corruption

A young clerk peruses the court's files.
Somewhere along the table, a fly zzzzz past with the car's horns
blaring outside.

The young clerk is tense;
5   that image of a pregnant wife
lying
painfully
hungrily
at the Ocean Road Hospital bed
10   whispers something in his heart's ears

'Destroy the file for me' zooms the rapacious voice
of the big-bellied man who just left him a while ago;
the appeal limps in his veins
waving a flag of those red-pinkish 1,000 shillings notes

15   no more pains
no more taxi-worries
the mother shall carry the new-born baby home
comfortably

Suddenly the court's file is in shreds.
20   Its white smiling pieces laugh loudly
applauding
the wish
of the rich bureaucrat
that has just been
25   implemented.

Freddy Macha *Tanzania*

A prescription for development

Our National General Assembly
was in deep mortification.
An insensitive journalist
(from some northern region)
5   had branded our country
a model of Underdevelopment.

How to gain recognition
as a developed nation
pondered our President.
10   The answer? – Commission
a group of technocrats
to study, possibly remedy
this intolerable situation.

Months and seminars later they
15   outlined their prescription:

What you have here, sir
are too many green hills –
a surfeit of lush vegetation.
Trees are fine but unproductive
20   and hills are an impediment.

There are too many canefields
and too many plantations.
We do not know what development
is, but an agricultural economy
25   is the badge of underdevelopment.

Your beaches are beautiful, sir
but lack utilisation;
there are no tourists, hotels
or any high-rise apartments.

30   Your street are traffic-free
and your towns too quiet;
your people seem stress-free
and a trifle too contented.

They eat fruits and vegetable
35   and drink natural water
which we're shocked to discover
is indecently clean and pure.

So what we recommend, sir –
for your race to development –
40 is first massive deforestation
followed by massive importation.

You need juggernauts, bull-
dozers and belching factories
condos and fast-food chains
45 and hordes of snooping tourists.

You must import mineral water
and a medium-sized nuclear reactor;
and a score of foreign psychiatrists
to service your expat industrialists.

50 We beg your pardon, but pollution
is the hallmark of development.
To qualify as an advanced country
you have to boast a proper degree
of noise/smog/dumps and derangement

55 With no hesitation, our President
embraced their recommendation.
In ear-muffs he now sits
in a haze-shrouded apartment.

High above, but not quite beyond
60 the city's teeming shout and bustle;
with a glass of Perrier water
he pops tranquillisers by the bottle.

Cecil Rajendra *India*

technocrats (11): experts
condos (44): short for 'condominiums' –
luxury housing
expat (49): short for 'expatriate' – someone
who comes from overseas to work in a
country, for a period of time
smog; derangement (54): thick polluted air;
madness
Perrier water (62): imported, bottled mineral
water

from Song of Ocol

I have a nice house
In the Town,
My spacious garden
Explodes with jacaranda and roses,
5 I have lilies, bougainvillea, canna ...

Do you appreciate the beauty
Of my roses?
Or would you rather turn
My flower garden
10 Into a maize shamba?

What did you reap
When uhuru ripened
And was harvested?

Is it my fault
15 That you sleep
In a hut
With a leaking thatch?

Do you blame me
Because your sickly children
20 Sleep on the earth
Sharing the filthy floor
With sheep and goats?

Okot p'Bitek *Uganda*

uhuru (12): here, national independence

A pregnant schoolgirl

He paid for her seat in the matatu
And walked away;
As he disappeared in the city crowd
All her dreams vanished;

5   One more passenger squeezed in
And lit a cigarette,
She opened the window
And spat cold saliva out,
As the cigarette smoke intensified
10 She wanted to vomit:

She remembered the warm nights
When she was her man's pet,
She remembered the promises
The gifts, the parties, the dances –

15 She remembered her classmates at school
Who envied her expensive shoes,
Lipstick, wrist watch, handbag
Which she brought to school
After a weekend with him

20 The future stood against her
Dark like a night without the moon,
And silent like the end of the world;

As the matatu sped away from the city
She began to tremble with fear
25 Wondering what her parents would say;

With all hope gone
She felt like a corpse
going home to be buried.

Everett Standa *Kenya*

The natural world

The natural world

This section looks at the natural environment, and our relationship with our surroundings. The first poem observes different kinds of animals – the hunter and the hunted.

■ How is *A leopard lives in a muu tree* different from the Yoruba poem?

■ The two poems *Bats* and *Guardian fly* illustrate ways in which the writer relates to rather unlikely creatures. Is the first of these poems really about bats? What else might it be about? Anthony Nazombe describes his 'guardian' with accuracy and humour. Try writing a praise poem of your own to an animal (or some other aspect of the natural environment) you are familiar with.

■ *Carrion crows* and *Hawk roosting* make an interesting contrast. In the first, A.J. Seymour records his personal sensitivity to these 'emperors of the sky'. The second is about a similar bird of prey – but how is the poem very different? What may Ted Hughes be suggesting about one side of human nature?

■ The whale is an animal which has been hunted almost to extinction. Kit Wright makes a protest; how does he work on our feelings to do this? What is the anonymous author of *The red cockatoo* protesting about?

■ The remaining poems in this section are about our natural environment. The poems on page 66 vividly record the seasons in our own familiar environment. Which of these do you like best and why?

■ *Hymn to the sea* takes us to the small island of Barbados in the Caribbean Sea. The poet's use of language helps us to share his strong feelings for his native land. What would you want to mention if you were to write a similar poem about your home?

Kob antelope

A creature to pet and spoil
An animal with a smooth neck,
You live in the bush without getting lean.
You are plump like a newly wedded wife.
5 You have more brass rings round your neck
Than any woman.
When you run you spread fine dust
Like a butterfly shaking its wings.
You are beautiful like carved wood.
10 Your eyes are gentle like a dove's.
Your neck seems long, long
To the covetous eyes of the hunter.

Yoruba *Nigeria*

A leopard lives in a Muu tree

A leopard lives in a Muu tree
Watching my home
My lambs are born speckled
My wives tie their skirts tight
5   And turn away –
Fearing mottled offspring.
They bathe when the moon is high
Soft and fecund
Splash cold mountain stream water on their nipples
10   Drop their skin skirts and call obsenities.
I'm besieged
I shall have to cut down the muu tree
I'm besieged
I walk about stiff
15   Stroking my loins
A leopard lives outside my homestead
Watching my women
I have called him elder, the one-from-the-same-womb
He peers at me with slit eyes
20   His head held high
My sword has rusted in the scabbard.
My wives purse their lips
When owls call for mating
I'm besieged
25   They fetch cold mountain water
They crush the sugar cane
But refuse to touch my beer horn.
My fences are broken
My medicine bags torn
30   The hair on my loins is singed
The upright post at the gate has fallen
My women are frisky
The leopard arches over my homestead
Eats my lambs
35   Resuscitating himself.

Jonathan Kariara *Kenya*

Bats

A bat is born
Naked and blind and pale.
His mother makes a pocket of her tail
And catches him. He clings to her long fur
5 By his thumbs and toes and teeth.
And then the mother dances through the night
Doubling and looping, soaring, somersaulting –
Her baby hangs on underneath.
All night, in happiness, she hunts and flies.
10 Her high sharp cries
Like shining needlepoints of sound
Go out into the night and, echoing back.
Tell her what they have touched.
She hears how far it is, how big it is.
15 Which way it's going:
She lives by hearing.
The mother eats the moths and gnats she catches
In full flight; in full flight
The mother drinks the water of the pond
20 She skims across. Her baby hangs on tight.
Her baby drinks the milk she makes him
In moonlight or starlight, in mid-air.
Their single shadow, printed on the moon
Or fluttering across the stars,
25 Whirls on all night; at daybreak
The tired mother flaps home to her rafter.
The others all are there.
They hang themselves up by their toes.
They wrap themselves in their brown wings.
30 Bunched upside-down, they sleep in air,
Their sharp ears, their sharp teeth, their quick sharp faces
Are dull and slow and mild.
All the bright day, as the mother sleeps.
She folds her wings about her sleeping child.

Randall Jarrell *England*

Guardian fly

I shall sing a praise song
To my guardian fly; crosswinged
He takes off upon my walking
Having listened to my dreams
5   And followed saliva across the cheek.

When for the shower room I leave
Or for the dining hall
He rides on my shoulder
From time to time
10   Whispering advice into my ear.

He perches on the toilet soap
While water flows down my back.
He presides over the taking of soup
And announces fish from a mile away.

15   Sometimes when he is bored stiff
He invites friends to join the watch
My nose and hair are theirs
Only I am drawn into their arguments
Slapping myself in the process.

20   In the evening, weary but satisfied
He takes his usual stand
Mops his brow after the daylong chase
And with a long sigh
Looks on as I drift into sleep
25   'Good night my guardian fly', I pray.

Anthony Nazombe *Malawi*

Animals

I think I could turn and live with animals, they are
   so placid and self-contained;
I stand and look at them long and long.

They do not sweat and whine about their condition;
They do not lie awake in the dark and weep for
   their sins;

5 They do not make me sick discussing their duty to
   God;
Not one is dissatisfied – not one is demented with the
   mania of owning things;

Not one kneels to another, nor to his kind that lived
   thousands of years ago;
Not one is respectable or industrious over the whole
   earth.

Walt Whitman *U.S.A.*

Carrion crows

Yes, I have seen them perched on paling posts –
Brooding with evil eyes upon the road,
Their black wings hooded – and they left these roosts

When I have hissed at them. Away they strode
5 Clapping their wings in a man's stride, away
Over the fields. And I have seen them feast
On swollen carrion in the broad eye of day,
Pestered by flies, and yet they never ceased.

But I have seen them emperors of the sky,
10 Balancing gracefully in the wind's drive
With their broad sails just shifting, or again
Throwing huge shadows from the sun's eye
To brush so swiftly over the field's plain,
And winnowing the air like beauty come alive.

A.J. Seymour *Guyana*

Hawk roosting

I sit in the top of the wood, my eyes closed.
Inaction, no falsifying dream
Between my hooked head and hooked feet:
Or in sleep rehearse perfect kills and eat.

5   The convenience of the high trees!
The air's buoyancy and the sun's ray
Are of advantage to me;
And the earth's face upward for my inspection.

My feet are locked upon the rough bark.
10   It took the whole of Creation
To produce my foot, my each feather;
Now I hold Creation in my foot

Or fly up, and revolve it all slowly –
I kill where I please because it is all mine.
15   There is no sophistry in my body;
My manners are tearing off heads –

The allotment of death.
For the one path of my flight is direct
Through the bones of the living.
20   No arguments assert my right:

The sun is behind me.
Nothing has changed since I began.
My eye has permitted no change.
I am going to keep things like this.

Ted Hughes *England*

The song of the whale

Heaving mountain of the sea,
Whale, I heard you
Grieving.

Great whale, crying for your life,
5 Crying for your kind, I knew
How we would use
Your dying:

Lipstick for our painted faces;
Polish for our shoes.

10 Tumbling mountain in the sea,
Whale, I heard you
Calling.

Bird-high notes, keening, soaring:
At their edge a tiny drum
15 Like a heartbeat.

We would make you
Dumb.

In the forest of the sea,
Whale, I heard you
20 Singing.

Singing to your own kind.
We'll never let you be.
Instead of life we choose

Lipstick for our painted faces
25 *Polish for our shoes.*

Kit Wright *England*

keening (13): wailing, crying sound

THE POETRY LIBRARY

The red cockatoo

Sent as a present from Annam —
A red cockatoo.
Coloured like the peach-tree blossom,
Speaking with the speech of men.
5   And they did to it what is always done
To the learned and eloquent.
They took a cage with stout bars
And shut it up inside.

Anonymous *China*
Translated from the Chinese by Arthur Waley

An African thunderstorm

From the west
Clouds come hurrying with the wind
Turning sharply
Here and there
5   Like a plague of locusts
Whirling,
Tossing up things on its tail
Like a madman chasing nothing

Pregnant clouds
10   Ride stately on its back,
Gathering to perch on hills
Like sinister dark wings;
The wind whistles by
And trees bend to let it pass.

15   In the village
Screams of delighted children,
Toss and turn
In the din of the whirling wind,
Women —

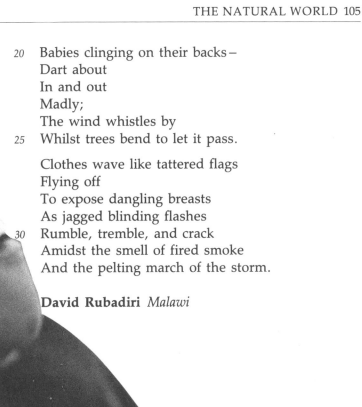

20 Babies clinging on their backs —
Dart about
In and out
Madly;
The wind whistles by
25 Whilst trees bend to let it pass.

Clothes wave like tattered flags
Flying off
To expose dangling breasts
As jagged blinding flashes
30 Rumble, tremble, and crack
Amidst the smell of fired smoke
And the pelting march of the storm.

David Rubadiri *Malawi*

August break

After three months of long rains
The land is a sodden bed
Of dried pond. The tarred roads shine
Fine threads of steam into the air.

5　The playgrounds jump and chatter
With the presence of children
In games abandoned yesterday
When the sky was falling tears.

The streets bustle with vendors,
10　Calling their wares by sweet names;
And the radio shops yell out
The rival sounds of Highlife.

Okogbule Wonodi *Nigeria*

The dry season

The year is withering; the wind
Blows down the leaves;
Men stand under the eaves
And overhear the secrets
5　Of the cold dry wind,
Of the half-bare trees.

The grasses are tall and tinted,
Straw-gold hues of dryness,
And the contradicting awryness,
10　Of the dusty roads a-scatter
With pools of colourful leaves,
With ghosts of the dreaming year.

And soon, soon the fires,
The fires will begin to burn,
15　The hawk will flutter and turn
On its wings and swoop for the mouse,
The dogs will run for the hare,
The hare for its little life.

Kwesi Brew *Ghana*

Hymn to the sea

Like all who live on small islands
I must always be remembering the sea,
Being always cognisant of her presence; viewing
Her through apertures in the foliage; hearing,
5 When the wind is from the south, her music, and smelling
The warm rankness of her; tasting
And feeling her kisses on bright sunbathed days:
I must always be remembering the sea.

Always, always the encircling sea,
10 Eternal: lazylapping, crisscrossed with stillness;
Or windruffed, aglitter with gold; and the surf
Waist-high for children, or horses for Titans;
Her lullaby, her singing, her moaning; on sand,
On shingle, on breakwater, and on rock;
15 By sunlight, starlight, moonlight, darkness:
I must always be remembering the sea.

Go down to the sea upon this random day
By metalled road, by sandway, by rockpath,
And come to her. Upon the polished jetsam,
20 Shell and stone and weed and saltfruit
Torn from the underwater continents, cast
Your garments and despondencies; re-enter
Her embracing womb: a return, a completion.
I must always be remembering the sea.

25 Life came from the sea, and once a goddess arose
Fullgrown from the saltdeep; love
Flows from the sea, a flood; and the food
Of islanders is reaped from the sea's harvest.
And not only life and sustenance; visions, too,
30 Are born of the sea: the patterning of her rhythm
Finds echoes within the musing mind.
I must always be remembering the sea.

Symbol of fruitfulness, symbol of barrenness,
Mother and destroyer, the calm and the storm!
35 Life and desire and dreams and death
Are born of the sea; this swarming land
Her creation, her signature set upon the salt ooze

To blossom into life; and the red hibiscus
And the red roofs burn more brightly against her blue.
40   I must always be remembering the sea.

Frank Collymore *Barbados*

cognisant (3): aware, knowing
rankness (6): strong smell
Titans (12): giants
jetsam (19): sunken objects, washed ashore by the sea

This is war

From earliest times fighting men have sung or chanted war songs as they went into battle. On their return, they have used poetry and song to celebrate their courage and their exploits and to mourn their dead. The first poem is a fine example of such a traditional song. How could you read it together most effectively?

■ There is another side to war. *The white horse*, a Chinese poem written a thousand years ago, reminds us more of the suffering from 'war and disorder' than the heroics.

■ In some ways we still celebrate war as heroic: war films, for example, are always popular at the cinema and on TV. But in *Geography lesson* Zulfikar Ghose expresses the puzzlement many of us share at continued senseless conflicts.

In this century poets have been particularly concerned with the horrors and futility of war. This is perhaps because in the twentieth century weapons of warfare have become more powerful, destructive and impersonal. Moreover, in modern warfare, civilians have often been in the front line. Chinua Achebe's poem on page 114 brings home powerfully the plight of innocent people caught up in war. *Moon in the bucket* protests at the 'murk and dirt' of war, and *Voices* makes a striking contrast between the calls of war and 'duty'.

Battle hymn

We are poured on the enemy like a mighty torrent:
We are poured like a river in spate when the rain is in the
  mountains.
The water hisses down the sands, swirling, exultant, and the
  tree that stood in its path is torn up quivering.
It is tossed from eddy to eddy.
5 We are poured on the enemy and they are bewildered.
They look this way and that seeking escape, but our spears
  fall thickly about them.
Our spears cling to their bodies and they are routed.
They look this way and that for deliverance, but they cannot
  escape us, the avengers, the great killers.
God of our fathers, guide our spears, our spears which thy
  lilac has touched.
10 They are anointed with sacrifice, with the sacrifice of
  unblemished kids, consecrate and hallowed by the nightjar
  of good omen.
Help us, high Spirit. Slay with us.
Let death come to their ranks, let the villages mourn their
  lost warriors.
Let their villages be desolate, let them echo with the cry of
  mourning.
We shall return rejoicing; and the lowing of cattle is in our
  ears.
15 The lowing of innumerable cattle will make glad our hearts.

Acholi *Uganda*

The white horse

Out of the North-east
galloped a white charger
with saddle empty, but
sticking into it, two arrows!

5 Pity the rider lost!
For who can now admire
his spirited prancing?

Last night he was the general
giving orders for battle;
10 just now he was killed;

war and its disorder bring death
through many doors.

cries of bitterness, and tears
like sleet in a winter's storm.

Tu Fu *China*
Translated by Rewi Alley
sleet (14): frozen rain

Geography lesson

When the jet sprang into the sky,
it was clear why the city
had developed the way it had,
seeing it scaled six inches to the mile.
5 There seemed an inevitability
about what on ground had looked haphazard,
unplanned and without style
when the jet sprang into the sky.

When the jet reached ten thousand feet,
10 it was clear why the country
had cities where rivers ran
and why the valleys were populated.
The logic of geography –
that land and water attracted man –
15 was clearly delineated
when the jet reached ten thousand feet.

When the jet rose six miles high,
it was clear that the earth was round
and that it had more sea than land.
20 But it was difficult to understand
that the men of the earth found
causes to hate each other, to build
walls across cities and to kill.
From that height, it was not clear why.

Zulfikar Ghose *Pakistan*

Refugee mother and child

No Madonna and Child could touch
that picture of a mother's tenderness
for a son she soon will have to forget.

5 The air was heavy with odours
of diarrhoea of unwashed children
with washed-out ribs and dried-up
bottoms struggling in laboured
steps behind blown empty bellies. Most
mothers there had long ceased
10 to care but not this one; she held
a ghost smile between her teeth
and in her eyes the ghost of a mother's
pride as she combed the rust-coloured
hair left on his skull and then –
15 singing in her eyes – began carefully
to part it ... In another life this
would have been a little daily
act of no consequence before his
breakfast and school; now she
20 did it like putting flowers
on a tiny grave.

Chinua Achebe *Nigeria*

Moon in the bucket

Look!
Look out there
in the bucket
the rusty bucket
5   with water unclean

Look!
A luminous plate is floating –
The moon, dancing to the gentle night wind
Look! all you who shout across the wall
10   with a million hates. Look at the dancing moon
It is peace unsoiled by the murk
and dirt of this bucket war.

Gabriel Imomotime Okara *Nigeria*

Voices

They speak of taxes
Of oil and power

They speak of honour
And pride of tribe

5   They speak of war
Of bows and arrows

They speak of tanks
And putrid human flesh

I sing my love
10   For Maria.

Ken Saro-Wiwa *Nigeria*

Conquerors

By sundown we came to a hidden village
Where all the air was still
And no sound met out tired ears, save
For the sorry drip of rain from blackened trees
5 And the melancholy song of swinging gates.
Then through a broken pane some of us saw
A dead bird in a rusting cage, still
Pressing his thin tattered breast against the bars.
His beak wide open. And
10 As we hurried through the weed-grown street,
A gaunt dog started up from some dark place
And shambled off on legs as thin as sticks
Into the wood, to die at least in peace
No one had told us victory was like this:
15 Not one amongst us would have eaten bread
Before he'd filled the mouth of the grey child
That sprawled, stiff as a stone, before the shattered door.
There was not one who did not think of home.

Henry Treece *England*

A war-torn wife

This war!
I am tired
of a husband who never sleeps
guarding the home or on call-up
5 Never sleeping!

Maybe inside him he says
'I am tired of a wife
who never dies
so I could stop guarding.'

Chenjerai Hove *Zimbabwe*

Tramp

He trudges the streets of Blantyre
weighed down by his KAR 'medals';
pierced Coca-Cola bottle tops,
funeral bands and decorations, shouting:
5 *Africa for the Africans!* before tourists
their cameras clicking incessantly as
he recounts memories of the dark bomb shelters
in the last battle of Tanganyika:
cycling a stationary bicycle tied
10 to the roof to keep the lamp burning
the boys singing for morale and how
with pangas, bayonets and muscle
they 'trounced' the Germans for their masters.

He tramps from bar to bar, sack over shoulder,
15 gathering half-drunk bottles of Carlsberg beer
and cigarette butts from rich people's ashtrays
for the victory party that he will hold
with the spirits of his slain colleagues
whom he salutes in his solitary minute of silence
20 remembering Burma and cheap women in eastern brothels,
Zomba and Nyasa camps, cannon and thunder
on the wooded banks of the yellow river.

And when we shower him with tambala coins
for a thrill, he smiles, his glassy eyes smarting
25 and like a khaki robot he drills stiffly
for another war he only knows, fingers
his stars, black stripes, and softly weeps
for a wife violated in absence, his land gone,
the promised compensation he will not see.

30 We watch him burn into ash like a cigarette
as he talks of blood in the red strip of the banner,
the setting sun casting darkness over his lost land
all so green, all so green, yet gone, going;
And he sulks, murmuring of the blood spilt in the struggle,
35 of the bullets turned into bees in *Operation Dawn*
human targets melting into lakes and mirages in Mulanje
and the fifty innocents massacred mercilessly at Nkhata Bay.

And when we query him about the contents
of his sticky soiled sack, he answers: 'Promises'
40 and embraces his silence again.

Frank Chipasula *Malawi*

KAR (2): Kings African Rifles – an army regiment formed in colonial
times, drawn from several African countries
panga (12): machete, cutlass
trounced (13): beat severely

Today

Today
the war
has ended
the people sing
freedom has arrived
5   the people are singing
songs
of joy or
songs for the dead.

Chirwa P. Chipeya *Zimbabwe*

If I die in war

If I die in War
You remember me
If I live in Peace
You don't.

Spike Milligan *England*

THE POETRY LIBRARY

Reflections

Reflections

Maybe you have had a feeling or experience – of being alone and thoughtful, some time when the world around you seemed strange – perhaps when you wondered who you really were, why you were on earth and what life was all about? The poems in this section are particularly concerned with the mystery of those things we cannot see.

■ *The pond* evokes a situation where a young boy becomes reflective – perhaps by seeing, literally, his own reflection in a pond.

■ *Forefathers* also suggests the mystery of life, reminding us to keep more in touch with 'things' – the natural world – fire, water, trees than with 'beings'. What do you think these 'beings' are that we should pay less attention to? Does this poem persuade you of its truth?

■ We often make resolutions about what we are going to do in the future. What is Cecil Rajendra's comment on this in his poem on page 126? Think of five 'resolutions' you would like to make – and be able to keep! How do they compare with the resolutions members of your group have made?

■ *The new platform dancers* compares past and present. This is an excellent poem to read aloud. Discuss what sort of a 'voice' Jack Mapanje assumes in this poem: how would you bring this across? What is his view of the world he lives in? Do you sympathise with him at all?

■ Can you explain what Edwin Brock is referring to in each part of his poem on page 129? Do you think his view is too negative? What more positive views of the twentieth century might we have?

■ The poems *Lies*, *The people's creed* and *Thank you, Lord* all express beliefs and ideals. Do you share these beliefs? What other strong beliefs do you have?

The pond

There was this pond in the village
and little boys, he heard till he was sick,
were not allowed too near.
Unfathomable pool, they said,
5   that swallowed men and animals just so;
and in its depths, old people said,
swam galliwasps and nameless horrors;
bright boys kept away.

Though drawn so hard by prohibitions,
10   the small boy, fixed in fear, kept off;
till one wet summer, grass growing lush,
paths muddy, slippery, he found himself
there at the fabled edge.

The brooding pond was dark.
15   Sudden, escaping cloud, the sun
came bright; and shimmering in guilt
he saw his own face peering from the pool.

Mervyn Morris *Jamaica*

galliwasps (7): small lizards

Forefathers

Listen more often to things rather than beings.
Hear the fire's voice,
Hear the voice of water.
In the wind hear the sobbing of the trees,
5   It is our forefathers breathing.

The dead are not gone forever.
They are in the paling shadows
And in the darkening shadows.
The dead are not beneath the ground.

10   They are in the rustling tree,
In the murmuring wood,
In the still water,
In the flowing water,
In the lonely place, in the crowd;
15   The dead are not dead.

Listen more often to things rather than beings.
Hear the fire's voice.
Hear the voice of water.
In the wind hear the sobbing of the trees.
20   It is the breathing of our forefathers
Who are not gone, not beneath the ground,
Not dead.

The dead are not gone forever.
They are in a woman's breast,
25   A child's crying, a glowing ember,
The dead are not beneath the earth,
They are in the flickering fire,
In the weeping plant, the groaning rock,
The wooded place, the home,
30   The dead are not dead.

Listen more often to things rather than beings.
Hear the fire's voice,
Hear the voice of water.
In the wind hear the sobbing of the trees.
35   It is the breath of our forefathers.

Birago Diop *Senegal*

Dreams

Hold fast to dreams
For if dreams die
Life is a broken-winged bird
That cannot fly.
5 Hold fast to dreams
For when dreams go
Life is a barren field
Frozen with snow.

Langston Hughes *U.S.A.*

Burning log

i am
a burning log
my history being reduced
to ashes
5 what i remember
of yesterday
is the ashy taste
of defeat
my hope
10 for tomorrow
in the fire

Charles Mungoshi *Zimbabwe*

Changing the wheel

I sit by the roadside
The driver changes the wheel.
I do not like the place I have come from.
I do not like the place I am going to.
5 Why with impatience do I
Watch him changing the wheel?

Bertold Brecht *Germany*

New Year's Day

Today
the resolutions
(and so little time
for so many intentions)

5 I will be good
I will work hard
I will beat
my wife less often
I shall snarl less
10 Smile more
I will be a little more
generous with my affections

I will diet
I'll do my exercises
15 I will cut my drinking
Give up smoking
I will be a little less
boring in my conversations

I will stop the bombing
20 Start negotiating
Halt the killing
Commence healing
I will try
not to hurt man or animal

25 I will ... I will ...

Today's
the day
for resolutions
and the resolutions
30 come flooding in
for tomorrow
Tomorrow
the betrayals begin

Cecil Rajendra *India*

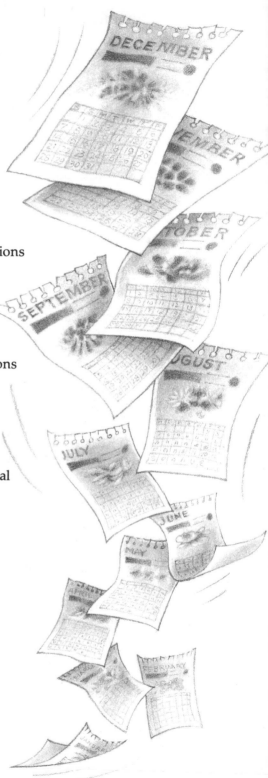

The new platform dances

Haven't I danced the big dance
Compelled the rain so dust could
Soar high above like when animals
Stampede? Haven't I in animal
5 Skins wriggled with amulets
Rattled with anklets
Scattered nervous women
With snakes around my neck
With spears in these hands
10 Then enticed them back
With flywhisk's magic?
Haven't I moved with all
Concentric in the arena
To the mystic drums
15 Dancing the half-nude
Lomwe dance
Haven't I?

Haven't my wives at mortars sang
Me songs of praise, of glory,
20 How I quaked the earth
How my skin trembled
How my neck peaked
Above all dancers
How my voice throbbed
25 Like the father-drum
I danced to
Haven't they?

Now, when I see my daughters writhe
Under cheating abstract
30 Voices of slack drums, ululate
To babble-idea-men-masks
Without amulets or anklets,
Why don't I stand up
To show them how we danced
35 Chopa, how IT was born?

Why do I sit still
Why does my speech choke
Like I have not danced
Before? Haven't I
40   Danced the bigger dance?
Haven't I?

Jack Mapanje *Malawi*

Lies

Telling lies to the young is wrong.
Proving to them that lies are true is wrong.
Telling them that God's in his heaven
and all's well with the world is wrong.
5   The young know what you mean. The young are people.
Tell them the difficulties that can't be counted,
and let them see not only what will be
but see with clarity these present times.
Say obstacles exist they must encounter
10   sorrow happens, hardship happens.
The hell with it. Who never knew
the price of happiness will not be happy.
Forgive no error you recognise,
it will repeat itself, increase,
15   and afterwards our pupils
will not forgive in us what we forgave.

Yevgeny Yevtushenko *Russia*

Five ways to kill a man

There are many cumbersome ways to kill a man:
you can make him carry a plank of wood
to the top of a hill and nail him to it. To do this
properly you require a crowd of people
5   wearing sandals, a cock that crows, a cloak
to dissect, a sponge, some vinegar and one
man to hammer the nails home.

Or you can take a length of steel,
shaped and chased in a traditional way,
10   and attempt to pierce the metal cage he wears.
But for this you need white horses,
English trees, men with bows and arrows,
at least two flags, a prince and a
castle to hold your banquet in.

15   Dispensing with nobility, you may, if the wind
allows, blow gas at him. But then you need
a mile of mud sliced through with ditches,
not to mention black boots, bomb craters,
more mud, a plague of rats, a dozen songs
20   and some round hats made of steel.

In an age of aeroplanes, you may fly
miles above your victim and dispose of him by
pressing one small switch. All you then
require is an ocean to separate you, two
25   systems of government, a nations's scientists,
several factories, a psychopath and
land that no one needs for several years.

These are, as I began, cumbersome ways
to kill a man. Simpler, direct, and much more neat
30   is to see that he is living somewhere in the middle
of the twentieth century, and leave him there.

Edwin Brock *England*

The people's creed

I believe in a colour blind God,

Maker of technicolour people,
Who created the universe
And provided abundant resources
5   For equitable distribution among all his people.

I believe in Jesus Christ,
Born of a common woman,
Who was ridiculed, disfigured, and executed,
Who on the third day rose and fought back;
10   He storms the highest councils of men,
where he overturns the iron rule of injustice.
From henceforth he shall continue
To judge the hatred and arrogance of men.

I believe in the Spirit of Reconciliation,
15   The united body of the dispossessed;
The communion of the suffering masses,
The power that overcomes the dehumanising forces of men.
The resurrection of personhood, justice, and equality,
And in the final triumph of Brotherhood.

Canaan Banana *Zimbabwe*

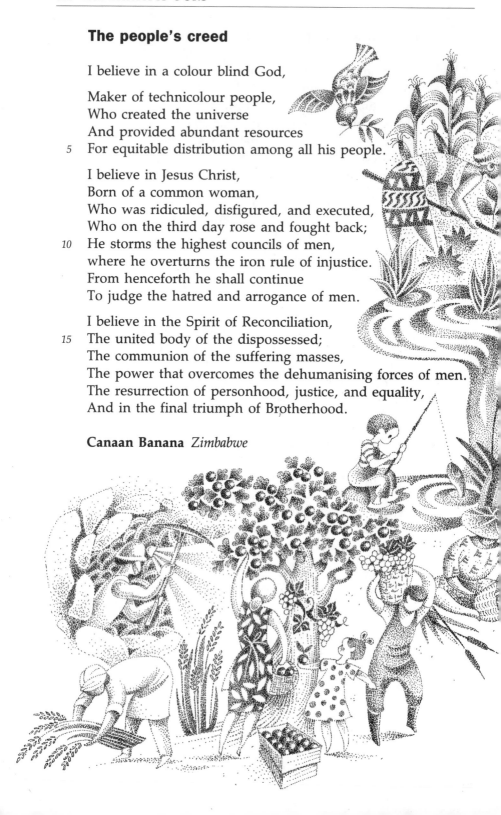

Thank you, Lord

I see You
Brown-skinned,
Neat Afro,
Full lips,
5 A little goatee.
A Malcolm,
Martin,
Du Bois.
Sunday services become sweeter when you're Black,
10 Then I don't have to explain why
I was out balling the town down,
Saturday night.

Thank you, Lord.
I want to thank You, Lord
15 For life and all that's in it.
Thank You for the day
And for the hour and for the minute.
I know many are gone,
I'm still living on,
20 I want to thank You.

I went to sleep last night
And I arose with the dawn,
I know that there are others
Who're still sleeping on,
25 They've gone away,
You've let me stay.
I want to thank You.

Some thought because they'd seen sunrise
They'd see it rise again.
30 But death crept into their sleeping beds
And took them by the hand.
Because of Your mercy,
I have another day to live.

Let me humbly say,
35 Thank You for this day
I want to thank You.

I was once a sinner man,
Living unsaved and wild,
Taking my chances in a dangerous world,
40 Putting my soul on trial.
Because of Your mercy,
Falling down on me like rain,
Because of Your mercy,
When I die I'll live again,
45 Let me humbly say,
Thank You for this day.
I want to thank You.

Maya Angelou *U.S.A.*

Malcolm (6): Malcolm X
Martin (7): Martin Luther King
Du Bois (8): W.E.B. Du Bois
Three famous African American leaders who fought for the
rights of the black population of the United States.
balling the town (11): having a noisy night out in the town

Acknowledgements

The author and publishers wish to thank the following who have kindly granted permission for the use of copyright material:

Edwin Brock for 'Five Ways to Kill a Man'.

Cambridge University Press for 'Kob Antelope' from *African Poetry* edited by Ulli Beier.

Mrs F.A. Collymore for 'Hymn to the Sea' by Frank Collymore.

Constable & Company Ltd for 'The Red Cockatoo' translated by Arthur Waley from *170 Chinese Poems*.

Ad. Donker, Publishers (Pty) Ltd for 'What's Wrong with People?' by Mongane M. Serote from *Selected Poems of Mongane M. Serote*, and 'Food for the Couple' by Mafikwa Gwala from *Voices from Within* eds Michael Chapman and Achmat Dangor.

East African Educational Publishers Ltd for 'Beloved of My Mother' and 'Song of Okot' by Okot p'Bitek from *Horn of My Love*.

The Estate of Sir John Squire for 'There was an Indian'.

Faber and Faber Ltd for 'Liu Ch'e' from *Collected Shorter Poems* by Ezra Pound, 'Bats' from *The Complete Poems* by Randall Jarrell, 'Hawk Roosting' from *Lupercal* by Ted Hughes, and 'Conquerors' from *The Haunted Garden* by Henry Treece.

Zulfikar Ghose for 'Geography Lesson' first published in *Jets From Orange* (Macmillan, London). Copyright © 1967 by Zulfikar Ghose.

Heinemann Publishers (Oxford) Ltd for an extract from Section 18 of *Letters to Martha and Other Poems from a South African Prison* by Dennis Brutus, 'Once Upon a Time' from *The Fisherman's Invocation* by Gabriel Okara, 'Refugee Mother and Child' from *Beware Soul Brother* by Chinua Achebe, and 'New Platform Dances' from *Chameleons and Gods* by Jack Mapanje.

David Higham Associates Ltd on behalf of Charles Causley for 'What has happened to Lulu?' and 'Ballad of the Bread Man' from *Collected Poems*; on behalf of the Estate of Langston Hughes for 'Ballad of the Landlord', and 'Mama and Daughter' and 'Dreams' from *Selected Poems*, and on behalf of Alice Walker for 'New Face' from *Revolutionary Petunias and Other Poems*.

Mrs. J.B. Jolobe for 'The Making of a Servant' by J. J. R. Jolobe.

Longman Group UK Ltd for 'To Mai' from *Thought Tracks* by Masaemura Bonas Zimunya.

MBA Literary Agents on behalf of the Estate of B. S. Johnson for 'The Song of the Wagondriver'. First published by Constable & Co. Ltd 1964. Copyright © 1990 by the Estate of B. S. Johnson.

Macmillan Publishing Company for a Shouh Berber extract from 'Gnomes'1, and a Berber extract from 'Love Songs' 11, from *The Unwritten Song*, Vol 1, edited with translations by Willard R. Trask. Copyright © 1966 by Willard R. Trask.

Mambo Press for 'One for the Road' by Charles Mungoshi from *Zimbabwean Poetry in English*, 'Grandma at 90 o'clock' by Eddison Zvogbo from *And Now the Poet Speaks* and 'Career Woman' by Charles Mungoshi from *The Mambo Book of Zimbabwean Verse*.

Spike Milligan Productions Ltd for 'If I Die in War' by Spike Milligan.

New Beacon Books Ltd for 'Love Is' and 'The Pond' from *The Pond* by Mervyn Morris (1973).
Oxford University Press for 'Reapers in a Mielefield' and 'An Abandoned Bundle' from *Sounds of a Cowhide Drum* by Oswald Mtshali (1971), and 'Ogun' from *Islands* by Edward Kamau Brathwaite (1969).
Penguin Books Ltd for and extracts from 'senryu' Anon. from *The Penguin Book of Japanese Verse* translated by Geoffrey Bownas and Anthony Thwaite. Copyright © 1964 by Geoffrey Bownas and Anthony Thwaite. 'Song of the Whale' by Kit Wright from *Hot Dog and Other Poems*. Published by Kestrel Books and Puffin Books. Copyright © 1981 by Kit Wright.
Peters Fraser & Dunlop Group Ltd on behalf of Roger McGough for 'Words ... Poems' from *In the Glassroom* published by Jonathan Cape Ltd (1976).
Cecil Rajendra from 'A Prescription for Development' and 'New Year's Day'.
Reed Book Services for 'Changing the Wheel' by Bertolt Brecht from *Poems 1913–56*, translated by M. Hamburger, published by Methuen London.
Mrs Elma Seymour from 'Carrion Crows' by Arthur James Seymour.
Société Nouvelle Presence Africaine
Everett Standa for 'Wedding Eve' and 'A Pregnant Schoolgirl' from *An Anthology of East African Poetry*, published by Longman Publishers (1988).
University of Iowa Press for 'My Baby Has No Name Yet' by Kim Nam-Jo, translated by Ko Won from *Contemporary Korean Poetry* (1970).
Virago Press Ltd for 'Woman Work', 'Still I Rise' and 'Thank You, Lord' by Maya Angelou.
Christopher van Wyk for 'Confession' and 'In Detention'.
Zimbabwe Publishing House (Pvt) Ltd for 'A War-torn Wife' by Chenjerai Hove.

The publishers have made every effort to trace the copyright holders, but if they have inadvertently overlooked any, they will be pleased to make the necessary arrangements at the first opportunity.

Photographic acknowledgements

The author and publishers wish to acknowledge, with thanks, the following photographic sources.

FORMAT Photographers Ltd pp27 (Val Wilmer); 31 (Maggie Murray); 53 (Maggie Murray); 68 (Maggie Murray); 93 (Maggie Murray); 95 (Connie Treppe); 121 (Jacky Chapman)

Magnum Photos Ltd pp11 (George Rodger); 18 (Don Charles); 45 (Gideon Mendel); 57 (Chris Steele-Perkins); 65 (Chris Steele-Perkins); 79 (Marc Riboud); 87 (Jean Gaumy); 105 (Chris Steele-Perkins); 109 (Gideon Mendel); 117 (Raymond Depardon)

The cover photograph is courtesy of Magnum/Eli Reed

Illustrations by Carine Hay

The publishers have made every effort to trace the copyright holders but if they have inadvertently overlooked any, they will be pleased to make the necessary arrangements at the first opportunity.